Exploring Science
IN YOUR
Home Laboratory

By RICHARD HARBECK

Illustrations and Photographs by the Author

THE FOUR WINDS PRESS · NEW YORK

To the many hundreds of boys and girls with whom he has had the pleasure of working, the author owes the inspiration for the ideas in this volume. Credit is also due the many professional associates who have given freely of their advice.

Finally, the author is well aware that this book could never have been developed and written without the patience and encouragement of a thoughtful wife and the constructive criticism of two interested teen-aged daughters.

Published by The Four Winds Press, a division of Scholastic Magazines, Inc., New York, N. Y.

Printed in the U.S.A.

PREFACE

Science is a curiosity catcher. Your senses "catch" the many natural curiosities all around you — the hardness of steel, the growth of a flower, the wind in the trees, the arc of a hard-hit baseball, the twinkling of a star. Every day you can see, hear, feel, even smell such things.

Then, in a curious way, these curiosities turn around and catch *you*. You find yourself asking: "Why does it happen? Why is it so?"

The purpose of this book is to help you satisfy some of your curiosity in a way that scientists have been doing for centuries: *by experiment*.

CONTENTS

INTRODUCTION

It's Easy to Set Up a Home Laboratory 7

Fields of Science That You Can Explore 8
Making Up Your Mind
about a Home Laboratory 9
How to Work in Safety 13
Build Your Laboratory Slowly 15

1. First Steps in Planning Your Laboratory 16

Family Approval Is Essential 16
Planning and Locating Your Lab 17

2. Building and Equipping a Laboratory Bench 23

Sketch before Building 23
The Laboratory Bench 25
Water Supply 32
Electricity and Gas 34
Waste Disposal 36

3. Outfitting Your Laboratory 39

Containers You Will Need 39
Equipment You Should Purchase 47
Equipment You Can Make 52
Materials 76

4. Procedures You Will Need to Know 79

Cutting and Bending Glass Tubing 79
Connecting Glassware 83

Weighing Chemicals 84
Measuring Volumes 88
Calculating and Preparing Solutions 89
Filtering 95
Heating Laboratory Glassware 97
Collecting and Handling Biological Specimens . . 98
Observing Living Specimens
    through the Microscope 101
Measuring Time 103

5. Some Ideas to Get You Started 105

  Some Things to Explore in Chemistry 107
  Some Things to Explore in Biology 110
  Some Things to Explore in Physics 113
  Some Things to Explore in Earth Science 115
  Some Things to Explore in Space Science 117

Appendix A. Some Common Chemical Compounds . 119

Appendix B. The Chemical Elements 122

Appendix C. Units of Measurement 124

Index to Illustrations 125

Index to Materials, Procedures, and Experiments 126

There are many new worlds to explore
in a well-planned home laboratory.

INTRODUCTION

It's Easy to Set Up a Home Laboratory

If you are like many young people, you've probably more than once had the urge to do some "experimenting." Perhaps you expressed it by building a one-tube radio, making some disappearing ink, or trapping and observing insects. Or perhaps you spent long hours with scientific kits, such as chemistry sets and microscopy labs. But whatever type of project you worked on, you undoubtedly found that it was a lot of fun to try something out just to see what might happen.

Experimenting is much more than a way of having fun, however — that is, if the experiment has been planned to answer a specific question. For then it becomes a tool of science, a key for unlocking the secrets of the universe. Nor does an experiment have to be complicated or expensive in order to be effective. Some of the most important scientific discoveries have been made with equipment and materials common enough to be found in most homes.

This book has been written to show you how easy it is to turn a corner of your home into a laboratory for scientific experiments. In it, you will find detailed instructions for selecting the best location for your lab, building a suitable bench to work on, and assembling and using the necessary equipment. Everything has been designed to be as inexpensive as possible. In fact, much of the required equipment can be salvaged from castoff household articles.

Fields of Science That You Can Explore

There is almost no field of science that cannot be studied profitably in a home laboratory. While it is true that your equipment will be limited, you'll be surprised at how much you can learn anyway. Of course, you aren't likely to make any discoveries not already known to scientists — at least, not at first! But the things you discover will be new to you and will teach you principles and techniques that you could learn in no other way.

It is possible to classify most areas of science in five fields: biology, chemistry, physics, earth science, and space science. Biology is the study of living things; chemistry deals with the composition of substances and the reactions by which they are changed into other substances; physics covers sound, heat, light, electricity, atomic structure, and mechanics. The structure and atmosphere of our earth are in the domain of earth science, while space science deals with astronomy, astronautics, and other problems of outer space. Neither of the last two is really a "basic" science, for each depends heavily on a knowledge of the first three.

In the last chapter of this book, you will find a list of suggested projects for investigation in your lab — as well as an introduction to scientific thinking. All five of the fields mentioned above are represented, but the list is far from complete. As you will discover after you begin work, one project will suggest another, and soon you'll be making long lists of your own. As a matter of fact, it will probably be hard to find time to carry out all of the projects and investigations that will occur to you.

Making Up Your Mind about a Home Laboratory

After you have read this far, but before you begin to think about setting up a laboratory of your own, you should decide whether you really want one. This might seem to be pretty obvious advice, but there's good reason for giving it. Gathering scientific materials and performing experiments will not only take up a good deal of your leisure time, but will make something of a dent in your allowance. And while you're bound to get a good deal of pleasure from your scientific efforts, a lot of hard work and study must be done too. If you're wondering about whether you have the ability to make and use scientific equipment, however, the following experiments have been designed to show you just how easy it can be.

For the first experiment, cut from a piece of white paper toweling a strip about 1/2 inch wide and 6 inches long. Wrap one end of the strip around a pencil and hold it in place with a paper clip, as shown in Fig. 1. Now suspend the strip, by the pencil, from the top of a glass tumbler, tearing off enough of the strip's free end so that it just touches bottom. Remove the strip and pour about an inch of water into the glass.

Very carefully put a small spot of ordinary blue writing ink in the center of the strip about 1½ inches from the free end. This done, immediately suspend the strip in the glass and observe what happens as the water slowly creeps up past the spot. The strip should remain suspended for at

Fig. 1. A Simple Experiment in Chromatography

least 15 minutes before being removed for drying. If you don't see bands of different colors, try again with another brand of blue ink. Should you use ink from a ball-point pen, pour rubbing alcohol into the glass instead of water.

The experiment you have just performed was based on a technique called *chromatography*. This technique is often used by biologists and chemists to separate and identify mixtures of certain types of chemicals. The different colors you saw were the various dyes that were mixed into the ink to give it its color. Similar results can be obtained with other colors of ink (although blue is usually the most interesting), and even with some fruit and vegetable juices.

Now let's try something a little different: making and using a simple microscope. All you'll need for its construction is a 12-inch length of soft wire (such as baling wire). Bend and twist the wire, as shown in Fig. 2, making each

10

of the two loops about 1/8 inch in diameter and as round as possible. Your microscope is now complete and can be used to study many liquid materials. For a starter, try looking at the water and sediment from the bottom of a puddle or pond.

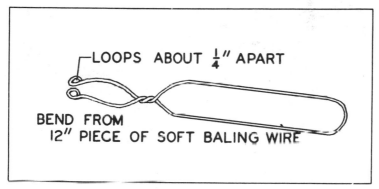

Fig. 2.   A Water Drop Microscope

To do this, scoop up some of the material in a dish and pick up a drop with one of the microscope loops. With the second loop, pick up a drop of clean water from another dish. Hold the clean-water loop close to your eye and look through it at the other loop. It will help if you look downward toward a sheet of illuminated white paper (see Fig. 3). If you don't see anything moving around in the loop of pond or puddle water, put a handful of dry grass into the first dish and wait a day or two before trying again.

Finally, just for fun, here's an experiment that requires no equipment at all! Take two sheets of notebook paper and hold them between your fingers, as shown in Fig. 4. Blow downward between the sheets, first gently, then as hard as you can. Are you curious about what happens?

Fig. 3.   Using the Water Drop Microscope

Fig. 4.   Another Simple Experiment

How to Work in Safety

If the foregoing experiments have intrigued you, and if you've decided to put the necessary time and work into a home laboratory, the next thing to think about is safety. Every year scores of boys and girls injure themselves while "experimenting." These accidents are unnecessary and can be avoided if simple precautions are taken. That's why the following list of safety rules has been included right here, in the introduction to this book. It is of the utmost importance that you understand these rules and take them seriously.

Rule 1. Never work in secret. A responsible person *always* makes certain that someone else knows where he is, but this is particularly important if he is working in a laboratory. Even the most careful experimenter can have an accident, and most accidents require prompt assistance from another person. **Never try any secret experiments!** Secrecy leads to nervousness, and nervousness almost guarantees an accident.

Rule 2. Always experiment with a purpose. A scientific experiment is carried out to test a possible answer to a question. Purposeless fooling is not only unscientific, but also dangerous. Most serious accidents in home laboratories are caused by "just messing around." Throughout this book, you will find many suggestions for safe laboratory procedures. Follow them, and you should never have any trouble.

Rule 3. Observe laboratory security. Unless your laboratory has been set up in partnership, you will find it wise (and not at all selfish) to keep it for your own exclusive use. This doesn't mean that you should not *show* it to anyone else; it merely means that people who are not skilled or seriously interested should not be allowed to meddle. Try to set up your laboratory so that it can be locked when you are away.

Rule 4. Watch what you store. It is necessary to be extremely careful about what you keep in your laboratory. Many a seemingly harmless material can be a fire hazard or the source of dangerous fumes. Here are some examples of things that *cannot* be safely stored in a home lab:

> Substances that decompose or oxidize (for instance, many kinds of oil)
> Highly volatile and inflammable liquids (such as gasoline)
> Explosive materials
> Loose papers
> Cleaning cloths
> Open bottles of chemicals
> Dirty glassware

Rule 5. Never keep anything in an unlabeled container. You don't have to be a particularly forgetful person to be confused about which of two identical, unlabeled bottles contains a certain chemical. Even if you are storing an unknown substance, you should label it accordingly. Be sure, also, to label boxes used to store small items of equipment. It will save you much rummaging around.

Rule 6. Never leave your laboratory in a dangerous condition. It is only common sense, for example, to be sure that all flames are out and all electrical apparatus turned off before you leave your lab. Don't rely on a hasty inspection; heating flames are often nearly impossible to see in a well-lit room and laboratory hot plates have covered elements.

Devices using either house current or batteries are usually not safe to leave unless the power has been disconnected. Bottles of chemicals and other odds and ends should not be left cluttering the bench or table top, but should be returned to their proper places.

Rule 7. Never start anything you haven't time to finish. This rule follows directly from Rule 6. If you want to do an experiment that involves heating a container of water, it would obviously be foolish to start work five minutes before your usual dinner hour. You would then be tempted to continue working — thus annoying your family — or to leave the burner dangerously unattended.

Build Your Laboratory Slowly

You are now ready to begin making plans for setting up your lab. As you read through the chapters that follow, it will be obvious that much of your planning will depend on what field of science interests you most. Of course, it might be hard to make a decision at first, and in any case many of the problems you'll be working on will involve more than one field. Unless you already have a strong desire to specialize, it would be well to start off as simply as possible. The more elaborate facilities and equipment can be added after you've been experimenting for a while and have a better idea of your needs.

CHAPTER 1

First Steps in Planning Your Laboratory

Your home laboratory can take any one of many different forms, because its size and nature will depend not only on the field of science to be studied, but also on the amount of available space. If you are an apartment dweller with limited room, remember that many experiments can be performed in a "lab" that is nothing more than a well-designed storage box. People with more room to spread out, however, should have the convenience of a specially built bench. Although the emphasis of this book is on the latter type of home laboratory, most of the ideas for experiments and homemade equipment can be used even in cramped quarters.

Family Approval Is Essential

Before making any decisions about what your laboratory will be like, you must enlist the cooperation of your family. Their sympathy and help will be essential to the success of a project in which you intend to invest so much of your time and effort. Your parents will especially appreciate your discussing with them the nature of the scientific problems you are interested in studying. Show them a list of things you will need to conduct your experiments, have them read the introduction to this book, and let them know that you understand the importance of sticking to the rules. If your father enjoys working with tools, he will probably be happy to help you build your facilities and equipment.

You'll be expected, of course, to share your laboratory with any brothers or sisters who are interested in science — but be careful about friends. If you have one or more science-minded friends, it certainly might be advantageous to form a partnership, but be sure that any prospective partner behaves properly in your home. He should not, for example, resort to loud words or violence for settling disagreements. Don't invite anyone to be a partner without first getting the *full agreement* of your parents. Similarly, anyone invited to be a partner should have the permission of his or her parents before accepting. And before a partnership is formed, there should be complete agreement that all laboratory rules will be carefully observed.

Planning and Locating Your Lab

Once you have obtained the complete support of your family, you are ready to get down to business. The following list of questions will help you make many of your first decisions. Your answers will determine the location of the lab as well as its size and general arrangement.

1. What kinds of equipment will be needed to carry out your experiments? Large pieces of equipment or complex experimental arrangements will require considerable bench or table area; adequate storage space must also be provided.

You will need convenient electrical outlets for some types of equipment; running water and drainage facilities for other types. An experiment using equipment of the latter kind might be simple enough to be set up and taken down in a few minutes. In that case, you could probably arrange, temporarily, to work on the drainboard of the kitchen sink. If the experiment is too complicated for this, however, you'll have to provide more permanent facilities or give up the idea of performing it.

2. *What types and quantities of chemicals will be used?* Regardless of what field of science you pursue, you'll probably be using chemicals. Small amounts of the few chemicals needed in certain types of biology or physics experiments present no special problems. But the amounts and kinds of chemicals needed for a chemistry laboratory are another matter. Labs of this type should have enough shelf space to store an ever-increasing number of bottles without dangerous overcrowding. The shelves will have to accommodate a wide variety of bottle sizes, and they should be sturdy enough to support heavy weights.

Many chemicals are highly corrosive, so a chemistry laboratory should never be located near fine floors, woodwork, furniture, etc. Even more important is the necessity for proper ventilation. Chemical fumes are often highly noxious and can be poisonous even in small amounts. Your parents will probably bring your scientific career to an abrupt end the first time you fill the house with hydrogen sulfide or with some other distasteful and easily produced gas. Ideally, ventilation arrangements should provide for air to move by the laboratory bench and out an open window. **Never set up a chemistry or biology laboratory in a closet or other windowless room.**

3. What kinds of heat sources will be required? There are very few laboratory situations in which some kind of heat source will not be needed. Open flames should be used only where there is sufficient working area to keep them away from walls and shelves. If you use electric heaters, you must provide electrical outlets of the proper current capacity.

4. How secure will your laboratory have to be? If you have young brothers or sisters, or if neighborhood children are frequent visitors to your house, be sure that your lab is not located where they can get at it. In any case, you should never keep valuable equipment and potentially dangerous substances in frequently traveled parts of the house. For this reason, hallways and garages are usually not suitable places for home laboratories.

It's doubtful that any location in your house will meet all of these requirements. Important deficiencies can often be corrected, however. For example, floors can be protected by placing a platform like that in Fig. 5 in front of your labora-

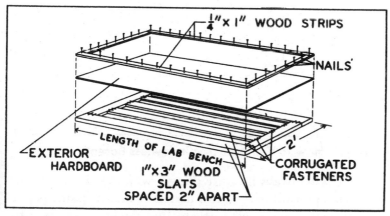

Fig. 5. A Protective Platform for Your Laboratory Bench

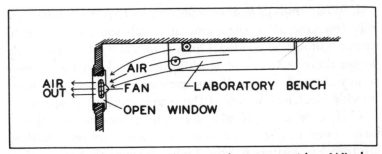

Fig. 6. One Way to Ventilate a Laboratory with a Window

tory bench. Note how the 1/4-by-1-inch wood strips form a "dam" to keep liquids from running off. A small electric fan facing an open window (Fig. 6) can help solve a ventilation problem. Ventilate a lab located in a windowless basement corner as shown in Fig. 7.

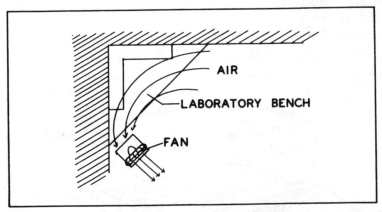

Fig. 7. How to Ventilate a Windowless Basement Corner

There will always be a fire danger wherever heat is to be used. One precaution you can take is to tack asbestos paper over all bench and shelf surfaces that might be exposed to heat from a flame or stove. But, just in case, keep a suitable fire extinguisher handy. A carbon dioxide extinguisher is best and can be picked up relatively cheaply in auto supply stores. Water is *not* suitable and should never be relied on. In addition, take a hint from school and industrial laboratories and keep an old, heavy blanket around. If your clothing should catch fire, you can smother the flames by wrapping yourself in it. There should be little possibility of fires from overloaded wiring if you install a fuse for the electrical outlets on your bench (Fig. 8). This fuse should have a lower rating than the one in the household circuit you are using, and it should never be larger than 15 amperes.

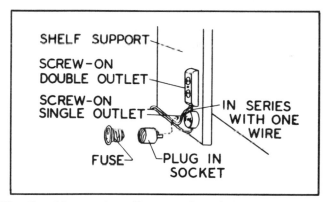

Fig. 8.   How to Install a Fuse for Electrical Protection

The security problem is probably the most difficult one to solve, especially if small children are around. If you cannot lock your lab, remember, at least, that children are easily attracted by almost anything they can see. Open doors and low benches or shelves will increase the visibility of your laboratory wonders. The simple hardboard screen illustrated in Fig. 9 will not only help insure privacy, but may also serve to prevent gusts of air from blowing across the laboratory bench.

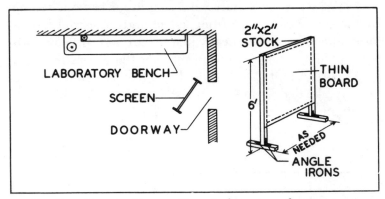

Fig. 9.   How to Screen Your Laboratory for Privacy

CHAPTER 2

Building and Equipping a Laboratory Bench

Once you have decided on the location, size, and nature of your laboratory, you are ready to think about actually building it. In this chapter you will find suggestions for the construction of a lab bench, a water supply, and other facilities. But, as you know, your exact needs will depend on the kind of experimentation you plan to do and the location you have available.

Consider the ideas contained here only guides. Although they certainly cover the basic requirements for any laboratory, they must be modified to fit your particular situation. For example, many of the dimensions given will have to be changed to suit the available space and materials. Use your imagination freely, and you'll come up with a bench that will serve you well for all present and future experimenting.

Sketch before Building

Make a careful sketch of your proposed laboratory before you so much as pick up a hammer. This effort will pay for itself many times over by saving you both time and materials. Although your sketch need not be a neat, detailed example of the draftsman's art, it should be drawn to scale. And you'll find the job much easier if you do your drawing on ordinary graph paper. Let the distances between each of the lines on the paper represent either 1 or 2 inches; then the distance between twelve lines will represent either 1 or 2 feet.

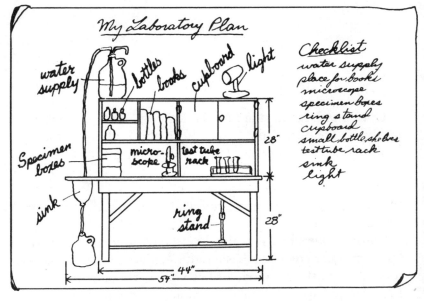

Fig. 10. A Typical Laboratory Plan

Figure 10 shows a sketch of a biology lab; the boy who planned it had to make use of a limited amount of space. Notice that a checklist of basic items was made first, and that although graph paper was not used the sketch was drawn to scale. A top view (not illustrated) was also drawn to show the depths of the bench top and shelves. Be sure to include provisions for the following kinds of things as you plan your laboratory:

1. Adequate working area (at least 2 feet deep by 3 feet long if you intend to use heat)
2. Proper bench height (32 to 38 inches for a chemistry bench, 28 to 32 inches for other benches)
3. Lockable cupboard for dangerous chemicals and equipment
4. Storage space for the various kinds and sizes of equipment to be used
5. Convenient shelves for reference books and lab notes
6. Cool, dry storage space for biological specimens (if needed)
7. Water supply and sink
8. Electrical outlets and lighting
9. Containers for waste disposal
10. Fire extinguisher, fire blanket, first-aid kit
11. Floor protection (if needed)
12. Ventilating fan (if needed)

The Laboratory Bench

A good bench is the first item of furniture you will need for your lab. Whether you start with an old table or build from the ground up, your bench should be as sturdy as possible. More than one home laboratory has come to an untimely end with the collapse of a makeshift table. A discarded table can be used in a home laboratory only if its legs and bracing pieces are solid and secure. If you plan to set storage shelves on it, be sure there is plenty of support. Glass, metal, and chemical materials are heavy, and an ac-

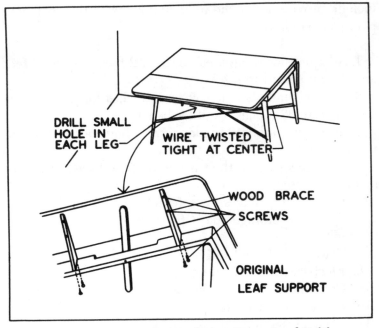

DRILL SMALL HOLE IN EACH LEG

WIRE TWISTED TIGHT AT CENTER

WOOD BRACE

SCREWS

ORIGINAL LEAF SUPPORT

Fig. 11. How to Strengthen a Drop-Leaf Table

cumulation of only a few months can easily amount to 100 or more pounds.

Figure 11 shows how an old drop-leaf kitchen or dinette table can be strengthened and made reliable. The wire prevents the legs from collapsing outward, while the braces keep one of the leaves locked securely in place. The other leaf should be removed, or folded down and placed against the wall. Never trust the wood or metal leaf supports already on the table. They will usually slip or break under a heavy load.

If you haven't an old table available, it's not too difficult to build a bench like that in Fig. 12. For a better working

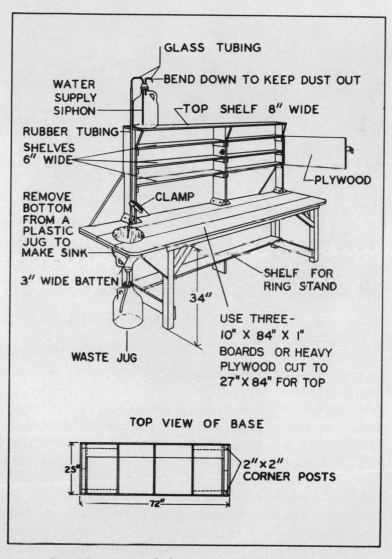

GLASS TUBING

BEND DOWN TO KEEP DUST OUT

WATER
SUPPLY
SIPHON

TOP SHELF 8" WIDE

RUBBER TUBING

SHELVES
6" WIDE

PLYWOOD

REMOVE
BOTTOM
FROM A
PLASTIC
JUG TO
MAKE SINK

CLAMP

3" WIDE BATTEN

34"

SHELF FOR
RING STAND

USE THREE-
10" X 84" X 1"
BOARDS OR HEAVY
PLYWOOD CUT TO
27" X 84" FOR TOP

WASTE JUG

TOP VIEW OF BASE

25"

72"

2" x 2"
CORNER POSTS

Fig. 12. A Bench for a Chemistry Laboratory

Fig. 13.   A Frame for a Laboratory Bench

surface, cover its top boards with thin plywood or hard-board. And if cost is no problem, use 3/4- or 1-inch plywood, omitting the boards entirely. A photograph of the bench frame appears in Fig. 13. Notice the use of 1-by-6-inch sheathing lumber around the top; this gives the bench great rigidity. The construction of the bench's shelves, cupboard, water supply, etc. will be explained later. These items, of course, can also be used with a modified table.

Whether you use a modified table or construct your own bench, the top should be protected from chemical damage. Most scientific supply companies, and many paint stores, carry a special black paint that resists chemical action. Follow the manufacturer's instructions exactly, and don't forget to paint your chemical storage shelves too. The bench that appears in the photographs has been left unpainted so that you can see its construction.

If yours is a biology lab, mount a large square of glass on the bench top after painting; it makes a fine surface for working on specimens. A single layer of dull, black cloth placed under the square will protect it from breakage and also provide a good background for observation. Hold the glass in place with glazier's points or short brads. The flat side of a screwdriver or pair of pliers can be used to press them in.

Shelves and Cupboards

The set of shelves in Fig. 12 (see also Fig. 14) was designed for a fairly large chemistry laboratory. Note that bottles of different sizes can be accommodated and that the cupboard door has a hasp for locking. Another arrangement of shelves, more suitable for a small biology laboratory, is shown in Fig. 15. Somewhat deeper shelves (Fig. 16) are usually needed for the materials and equipment employed in physics and earth science laboratories. The pegboard shown can be used for holding small tools, coils of wire, and other hard-to-store items.

Use boards 1 inch thick (actually these are only about 3/4 inch thick as obtained from the lumber yard) for all shelves. Place the vertical supports no more than 36 inches apart, and fasten the shelves to them as indicated in Fig. 17. Shelves held in place by nails driven through the supports are not safe; they will nearly always work loose in time.

Notice that the shelf supports of Figs. 12, 14, and 15 are prevented from wobbling sideways by triangular corner

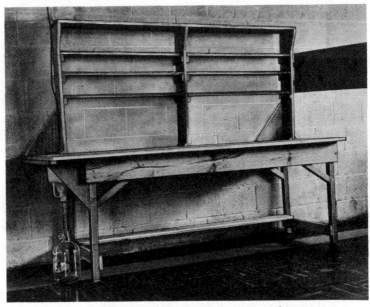

Fig. 14.   A Bench for a Chemistry Laboratory, Complete and Ready to Equip

braces. These extend along the whole depth of the supports and are held in place with long screws. A more expensive method, but one that is easier and better, is to nail or screw a large piece of hardboard across the backs of the shelves. One or two boards fastened diagonally across the backs will also provide a strong brace.

Any group of shelves can be converted into a cupboard by placing a hinged door in front of them. The center right-hand shelves in Figs. 12 and 14 have been used in this way. Small padlock hasps of the type shown are available at almost any hardware store. Incidentally, you'll save yourself many painful bumps and bruises if you install cupboard

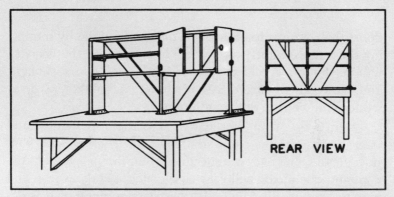

Fig. 15.   A Shelf Arrangement for a Biology Laboratory

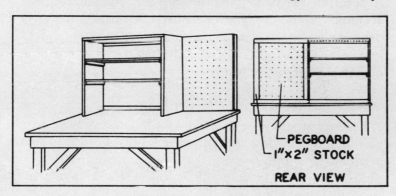

Fig. 16.   A Shelf Arrangement for a Physics
or Earth Science Laboratory

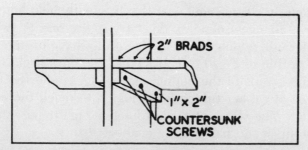

Fig. 17.   An Easy Way to Fasten Shelves in Place

doors that close automatically. This can be done by mounting the hinges slightly off vertical in such a way that gravity will do the job. Avoid the use of top-hinged doors, though. You won't always have a spare hand to hold them open while removing or replacing items.

To fireproof your cupboards, line the tops, sides, and backs with asbestos paper and cover the shelves with window glass. Don't ever use sheet metal for fire proofing. Many common chemicals will react with such metals as iron and zinc to produce hydrogen. It doesn't take much of this gas to form an explosive mixture with air; enough can easily accumulate in a cupboard that has been closed for several days. As a matter of fact, it's wise to provide several 1/2-inch ventilation openings near the top and bottom of any chemical storage cupboard.

Water Supply

Unless you are able to place your laboratory near a sink, you should provide a special water supply. Figure 14 shows a lab water-supply system that was constructed from the plan in Fig. 12. As you will discover, the arrangement is easy to set up and use.

The storage container shown on top of the shelf in Fig. 14 is a clean, 1-gallon-sized glass jug. It is almost impossible to properly clean a container that originally held household bleach, oil, or gasoline, so don't try to use one. A two-hole stopper into which two bent glass tubes have been inserted (not visible in Fig. 14) is placed in the jug's neck. One of the tubes runs to the bottom of the jug; connected to it is a piece of rubber tubing long enough to reach the edge of the sink. The other tube is just long enough to pass through the stopper and has nothing connected to it.

After the jug is filled with water, a syphon action is started by blowing through the open tube. Water will then flow through the rubber delivery tube until the jug is emptied or the tubing is clamped. A spring clothespin makes an acceptable clamp, particularly if it has been "beefed up" with a heavy rubber band. After the clothespin has been clamped onto the tubing, wrap the band several times around its jaws. Of course, you can also use a standard pinchcock clamp. These are available, quite inexpensively, at any laboratory supply house.

The sink shown in Figs. 12 and 14 is made from a gallon-sized, plastic liquid-bleach jug. Wrap the neck tightly with tape so that the pressure of a stopper will not crack the jug, and cut out the bottom with a sharp knife. Then cut an opening the exact size and shape of the bottom of the jug in the end of the bench (use a keyhole saw). Finally, fasten the jug in place with nails or tacks.

Don't expect a plastic-jug sink to last very long, especially if hot liquids are sometimes poured into it. However, it's a very simple matter to replace it every few months. If you can obtain a regular bowl-shaped sink not more than about 12 inches in diameter, by all means use it instead. Such a sink can be placed in a bench opening cut a bit smaller than the diameter of the sink's outside rim.

The bottom jug (also 1-gallon size) serves to receive liquid wastes poured into the sink. The rubber tubing leading to this waste receiver is connected to a short glass tube which, in turn, is pushed into a one-hole stopper. Insert the stopper tightly into the neck of the plastic jug (or the drain of the sink) from the *inside*. This will prevent the stopper from being forced out by water pressure. The waste receiver should be made of glass, but it need not be as scrupulously clean as the water-storage jug. Always empty the waste receiver when the water jug is filled, and you won't have to worry about overflowing.

If you plan to use distilled water, provide a second storage jug identical to the one already described. A turn or two of tape around the end of its delivery tube will serve to distinguish it from the tap-water jug. A waste receiver with a capacity of 2 gallons or more should then be employed.

If there's a chance that small children in the house will be tempted to tug on one of the tubes, you should fasten the jugs securely in place. This can be easily done with a pair of rubber strips cut from an old inner tube (Fig. 18); notice that they are crossed like a pair of suspenders. You don't have to uncross the strips in order to remove a jug for refilling; merely pull them out and down.

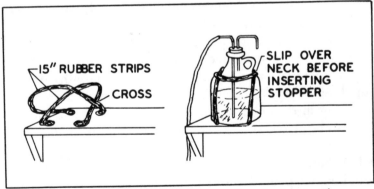

Fig. 18. How to Hold a Water Supply Jug in Place

Electricity and Gas

After you have built your laboratory bench, you will find it convenient to equip it with electric outlets. Simple screw-on outlets of the type illustrated in Fig. 8 are quite inexpensive, and can even be purchased with the wire already attached. Fasten them to the shelf supports, as shown, where they will be out of the way and safe from damage. If possible, provide one outlet in the center of the bench and another at the end farthest from the sink. Don't put an outlet where liquids might splash on it. For added protection, you will want to provide your electric outlets with low-amperage fuses, as described in Chapter 1.

Many chemistry and physics experiments call for a low-voltage source of direct current. This can be supplied by

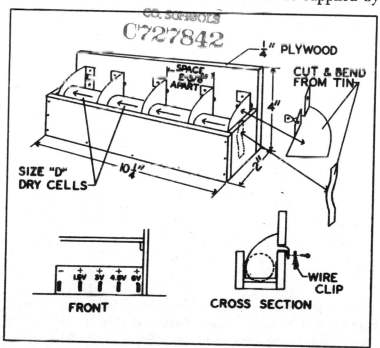

Fig. 19. A Low-Voltage Direct-Current Electricity Supply

one or more dry cells of the type used in flashlights. Figure 19 shows one way to assemble a battery of size "D" dry cells so that you can make connections to a number of different voltages. The arrows point to the positive, or "button," ends of the cells. Install the cells in the direction indicated by the arrows, and mark the terminals on the front panel as illustrated.

It is probably not practical for you to provide an outlet for a gas burner. Alcohol and electric heaters adequate for most laboratory purposes are described in the next chapter. If you *must* use a gas burner, and can afford it, purchase one of the small propane units designed for home workshops. When not in use, your propane burner should be stored away from heat and in such a manner that there is little danger of its rolling off a shelf and falling to the floor. With a little imagination, you can design and build a wood or wire rack to hold the burner securely.

Waste Disposal

No discussion of laboratory facilities would be complete without mention of the disposal of laboratory wastes. Accumulated wastes can produce serious fire hazards, extremely irritating odors, damage to equipment and furniture, and a very unscientific laboratory appearance. It is of the utmost importance that you observe the following procedures and precautions:

Scrap paper should never be allowed to clutter the laboratory bench. Get a small basket exclusively for waste paper, and empty it every day. Never put chemicals, broken glass, or biological specimens in this wastebasket.

Solid chemical wastes should be discarded into a wide-mouthed container made of crockery or enameled metal. Don't use glass or nonenameled metal containers for this purpose, and never mix moist solids or liquids with your dry wastes. At the end of each day, wrap the contents of the container in several layers of dry newspaper and discard in an outside incinerator or covered trash can.

Liquid chemical wastes, including the contents of the receiver below your lab sink, can usually be washed down any sink drain not equipped with a garbage-disposal unit. Run a lot of extra water down the drain after using it. Strong acids, however, should be neutralized before disposal of them in this way.

You can provide inexpensive facilities for neutralizing acids by filling a large-mouthed, 1/2-gallon jug with oyster shells, clam shells, or marble chips. Waste acids should then be poured *slowly* into the jar. When all bubbling ceases, the liquid can be washed down a sink drain as described above.

Rinse the shells or chips four or five times with plain water and set the jar aside until needed again. Even after a thorough rinsing, however, the chips will continue to produce carbon dioxide gas. Therefore, you should punch several holes in the jar lid — lest gas pressure build up to the point where the jar will burst.

Inflammable liquids should never be run down a sink drain. Many liquids of this kind do not mix with water and are so light that they collect at the top of the sink trap instead of being rinsed away. Pour inflammable liquids onto open, ungrassed ground far away from any building or tree. **Never attempt to dispose of them by burning.**

Broken glass should be swept up and immediately deposited in your outside trash can. Small slivers can be effectively picked up with moist paper toweling. Don't use your hand to brush them off the bench.

Biological specimens, such as dissected plants and animals, can usually be disposed of with your household food wastes. Don't allow these materials to gather in the laboratory. They will decay, attract insects and mice, and become very unpleasant to the other members of your family.

CHAPTER 3

Outfitting
Your Laboratory

Once your laboratory bench has been built and equipped with shelves, cupboards, and other facilities, you'll want to begin gathering the things needed for your experiments. Many of the materials and pieces of equipment described in this chapter are common to all of the sciences. Others are quite specialized and are needed for experiments in only one science. A great effort has been made to keep suggested materials as inexpensive as possible; few of them should result in much of a drain on your allowance.

Containers You Will Need

Regardless of what science you decide to specialize in, you will find use for many types and sizes of containers. An array of neatly labeled bottles and boxes makes things easy to find and adds much to the scientific atmosphere of a home laboratory. Poorly marked, lidless, and broken containers are disorderly, and therefore dangerous.

Most, if not all, of the containers you will need can be found in your home or those of your neighbors. After you have decided what you can use, it would be a good idea to make several lists for distribution to likely sources. Many people will be glad to save small jars, bottles, and plastic boxes for you. If you do ask your neighbors to save such items, however, be sure to collect them every few days. And when you have enough of any one item, pass the word. Busy people will not want to do you favors if *you* fail to cooperate.

Here are some ideas for containers that you can collect or make. Be sure to observe the precautions mentioned for the various kinds of jars, bottles, and boxes.

Containers for Chemicals

Solid and liquid chemicals are used in the laboratory study of nearly every science, so this category should interest almost everyone. Here is a list of general specifications for containers used to hold chemicals:

1. Neither the container nor its lid (or stopper) should react with the chemical to be placed in it.

2. The capacity of the container should not greatly exceed the quantity of chemical to be stored. However . . .

3. . . . the container should be large enough to be handled conveniently and not be easily misplaced.

4. It should be capable of being tightly closed to prevent contamination of its contents, leakage, or evaporation.

5. The container, especially if intended to hold a liquid, should not be easy to tip.

6. The container should be cleanable. As mentioned in

the last chapter, some common household materials cannot be removed from their bottles by ordinary cleaning procedures.

7. It should be durable. Chemicals should not be stored in ordinary cardboard boxes, for example. Substances such as sodium carbonate (washing soda) sometimes come packed in such boxes. These chemicals should be transferred to clean, dry, glass jars.

8. Containers for solid chemicals should have wide mouths; those for liquids should have small mouths.

9. Bottles with cork stoppers should be equipped with new ones of the proper size.

10. Opaque, green, or amber bottles should be provided for chemicals affected by light (such as compounds containing silver).

Mothers of very small children are one of the very best sources of containers for storing small quantities of solid chemicals. These are the variously sized glass jars in which baby food is sold. They can usually be obtained in large numbers, and their uniformity of size and shape makes for neat shelf arrangements.

A few larger containers will be needed to store substances bought in 1/2- or 1-pound packages. Mayonnaise, salad dressing, peanut butter, and jam jars can be used for this purpose. Very small amounts of solid chemicals can be stored in small glass pill vials. But these are difficult to label and easy to misplace, so use them sparingly.

Bottles suitable for liquid chemicals are more difficult to obtain. Many types, such as those holding certain medicines and cough syrups, cannot be completely cleaned. If, after thoroughly washing a bottle, you can still smell the original contents, it would be best to discard it. A friendly local druggist will often supply a dozen or so new bottles of various sizes for a few pennies apiece. Luckily, most liquid chemicals are sold in bottles that are quite suitable for lab storage.

Solutions of relatively strong acids should be kept in bottles equipped with glass stoppers. The usual type of laboratory acid bottle has a loose-fitting, ground-glass stopper, but it should never be used in a home where there are small children with busy fingers. Small amounts of acids are usually sold in bottles with glass-lined screw caps; these are quite safe from accidental spilling. Don't forget, however, that any bottle will break if dropped. Keep children out of your lab.

Discarded medicine-dropper bottles, when thoroughly cleaned, have many uses in the laboratory. To clean most droppers, carefully slip the rubber bulb off the end of the tube. Then use a glass rod to push the bulb inside out. Wash the two parts with hot soap and water, rinse, and allow to dry. Finally, turn the bulb right side out and replace it on the tube. The bottle itself should be cleaned as described in the paragraphs below.

All used jars and bottles intended for storing chemicals must be thoroughly washed and dried; usual dishwashing procedures will not suffice. The following technique should be followed instead; it will provide reasonable assurance of proper cleanliness. Plan to wash a sufficient number of containers at once so that you'll have enough to last for a while. Your mother won't appreciate your running to the sink every half hour or so to wash another bottle.

1. Fill a dish pan or sink with hot water and add soap or detergent. Try to avoid excessive sudsing.

2. Place the jars and bottles (tops removed) in the water. Then scrub their interiors with a brush and allow them to soak.

3. Discard labels as they soak off the glass, and wash away any remaining glue.

4. Carefully remove the linings from all covers with the tip of a knife. Scrub covers and linings, and let soak.

5. Remove the jars, bottles, covers, and linings, thoroughly rinsing each item under hot running water. Refill the pan or sink with fresh hot water and soak everything for at least an hour.

6. Remove the containers and lids from the water, and rinse as before. If they are to be air-dried, set them on a cloth-covered table or tray. To oven-dry the containers (covers and linings must be air-dried), place them on a metal surface, such as an aluminum cookie sheet. Then slide them into a cold oven (a hot one might cause some of the heavier containers to shatter) and adjust the temperature to not more than 250° F.

7. After about a half-hour, turn the oven off and allow it to cool completely. Remove the jars and bottles, insert the liners into the proper covers, and replace the covers (loosely) on the containers.

To mark your containers, use prepared gum-backed labels or cut labels from gum-backed paper. These should be made out before you stick them on the containers. Use waterproof ink, preferably black, to print the information. A typewriter does a neat job, but the letters are usually a little light and small. Labels for chemical bottles should contain the following information:

1. Chemical name of substance
2. Chemical formula (if a compound) or composition (if a mixture)
3. Common name, if any
4. Molecular or formula weight (see Chapter 4 and Appendix A)
5. Date obtained
6. Degree of purity (U.S.P., C.P., Tech.), if known

Important: Any bottle or jar containing a poisonous substance should have the word POISON printed in large red letters on its label. A separate POISON label (red) should also be fastened to the container. If it is possible for small children to get into your laboratory, all such containers should be kept in a locked cupboard like the one illustrated in Fig. 12.

Permanent labels should be protected from water, stains, and tearing. Clear lacquer does a good job, but the painted area should extend at least 1/4 inch onto the glass all around the label. Another method is to cover the label with strips of good-quality transparent tape. The tape should be pressed firmly onto the glass; otherwise it will tend to curl and peel off.

Containers for Biological Specimens

The types of containers needed for biological specimens vary widely with the nature of the material to be stored. Glass jars should be used to store material that must be kept immersed in a liquid or sealed from air and moisture. Dried

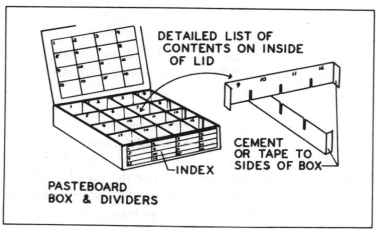

DETAILED LIST OF CONTENTS ON INSIDE OF LID

CEMENT OR TAPE TO SIDES OF BOX

INDEX

PASTEBOARD BOX & DIVIDERS

Fig. 20. A Specimen Storage Box

specimens can be kept in various kinds of plastic, wood, or pasteboard boxes. Manila envelopes make good containers for filing twigs, leaves, and small dried plants. Figure 41 shows how corners cut from envelopes can be used to store large winged insects for further study and mounting.

Compartmented boxes are very convenient for storing small dried specimens such as insects and seeds. These containers can be easily constructed from heavy pasteboard, as indicated in Fig. 20. Notice the method used to label and index each of the compartments. Compact and easy to stack, the boxes take up little room on a laboratory shelf.

It is particularly important that biological specimens be carefully identified on a label. Never rely on your memory. Labels, whether fastened to the container or directly to the specimen, should be clearly printed in black, waterproof ink and should contain the following information:

1. Scientific classification, if known
2. Common name, if known

3. Place collected
4. Date collected (and time of day, if important)
5. Other pertinent information, such as original weight, preservative, original color, etc.

If the size of the specimen or the nature of its container prevents including all of the necessary information on the label, then an index-card system should be used. Give each label a simple code number, and put the same number at the top of the index card containing the information. For easy reference, file the index cards in numerical order.

Containers for Mineral Specimens

Compartment trays provide the most convenient method of storing small mineral and rock specimens. Because of the weight of these materials, the trays should be made of wood or heavy plastic. Soil, clay, and sand samples should be stored in clean, wide-mouthed glass jars.

Mineral and rock specimens should be clearly and permanently marked with an index number as soon after collection as possible. Use black or white ink to print this number directly on the cleaned specimen. When the ink is dry, cover it with a small circle of clear lacquer, clear fingernail polish, or model-airplane cement of the nonwhitening kind.

Number a 3-by-5-inch file card to correspond with the index code on each specimen and fill in the following information:

1. Scientific name, if known
2. Common name, if known
3. Place collected (include depth, if collected underground)

4. Date collected

5. Other pertinent information, such as weight and chemical composition

Jars containing soil, clay, or sand samples should be similarly marked, but you can probably put all of the information on jar labels instead of cards.

Containers for Equipment and Supplies

Experiments involving such things as light, heat, sound, and mechanics usually require small items of equipment and supplies. Carbon electrodes, dry cells, short pieces of wire, wire connectors, screws, bolts, springs, solder, etc., are conveniently stored in small plastic boxes. Heavy pasteboard or wood containers (such as cigar boxes) may be used for larger materials.

Fragile or easily scratched items should be stored in boxes lined with cotton or flannel cloth. Roll long pieces of wire into coils before storing, and wind fine wire on spools. Screwdrivers, pliers, tin snips, and other small tools are hung from hooks inserted in a piece of pegboard (see Fig. 16).

Equipment You Should Purchase

Scientific work requires the use of many kinds of equipment. Some items can be improvised by the home experimenter — but others are so difficult to construct, or so inexpensive to purchase, that it doesn't pay to try. In the latter category are such things as test tubes, flasks, funnels, rubber and glass tubing, and microscope slides and cover slips.

These and other commonly used items are now stocked by many hobby supply stores. Equipment not available at hobby stores may be found at nearby scientific supply companies. (Check the classified pages of your telephone directory.) A few general suggestions for things you may need to purchase are given below. Your choice of the items listed will depend on what science you are studying.

Test Tubes

Test tubes are made from both "hard" and "soft" glass. The hard-glass tubes are more expensive than the soft, but do not have as great a tendency to break when heated suddenly. The soft-glass type, however, should be used for any experiment in which a tube must be deliberately broken.

Both kinds of test tubes are sold in a wide variety of sizes. The most convenient size for the home laboratory is 5 to 6 inches long and 1/2 to 3/4 inch in diameter. Test tubes for chemistry work should have a lip, while those for many biological purposes may be lipless.

Beakers

Because beakers are often used for heating liquids, they are usually made from hard glass. Standard beakers are sized by their volume in milliliters. A milliliter (abbreviated ml.) is nearly equal to a cubic centimeter (abbreviated cc.), and the two units are sometimes used interchangeably. The most convenient sizes will be 50 ml., 100 ml., and 250 ml. For storage purposes, a group of beakers of different sizes can be "nested" together.

Flasks

The flasks most often used in the average laboratory come in two shapes: Florence (round with a flat bottom) and Erlenmeyer (conical). Home experimenters usually find the Erlenmeyer flask most useful. Both kinds of flasks are available in a variety of sizes. Best for most experiments are the 100 ml. and 250 ml. units.

Funnels

Every laboratory needs at least one good glass funnel with a fairly long stem. The most versatile is one designed for use with 11-centimeter filter paper.

Thistle tubes are a type of funnel primarily used in gas-generation apparatus; they should never be employed for filtering. As the name implies, these units have tops shaped somewhat like thistles. The drawing at the upper right in Fig. 46 shows a thistle tube in use. Only one or two sizes are available in most retail stores; choose the one that seems most appropriate for the experiments you have in mind.

Glass Tubing

If you are primarily interested in chemistry, purchase 1 or 2 pounds of 6 mm. (outside diameter) soft-glass tubing. This amount will take care of your needs for quite a while. A smaller amount of tubing of the same size should be stocked by those interested in other sciences. Keep a few pieces of soft-glass tubing of a larger size on hand in any type of laboratory. Hard-glass tubing will probably be needed only on rare occasions.

Rubber Tubing

About 10 feet of small-diameter rubber (or flexible plastic) tubing will serve most laboratory needs. Be sure the size you get fits your 6-mm. glass tubing. Larger sizes are sometimes needed for use as delivery and drain tubes. These can be purchased as you need them.

Stoppers

Both rubber and cork stoppers are used in most laboratories. Cork stoppers are easy to bore or drill, and a bag of plain ones is relatively inexpensive. Rubber stoppers cost more, but are essential in many experimental situations. Buy a pound or two of mixed ones if you can. Since rubber is hard to bore, be sure the mixture includes a variety of one-hole and two-hole stoppers. You'll probably also need one or two stoppers with three holes; these should fit your flasks and gallon jugs.

Porcelainware

There may be times when you will have use for porcelain evaporating dishes, crucibles, and ignition boats. It is, however, frequently possible to find adequate substitutes for these around the house, so put them fairly low on your "to buy" list.

Microscope

If you intend to use a microscope to any great extent, get the most expensive one you can afford. But don't be fooled by such extras as battery-powered substage lights, extra-high magnification, and special trimming on the box. Judge a microscope by its lens system first, and stay away from a unit that distorts the image to any great degree. You can check distortion in the store by examining the gray area of a photograph in a newspaper under both low and medium powers. The rows of black dots you will see should be straight in all directions and must not be surrounded by fringes of color.

Most microscopes come equipped with either two or three objective lenses mounted on a turret. Keep in mind that you will rarely have use for the highest magnification of a three-power microscope. And a two-power microscope will probably be of somewhat better quality than an equally priced instrument having three powers.

Glass Slides and Cover Slips

These are obtainable in small, inexpensive packages. If you can afford it, purchase some recessed slides as well as plain ones. The former are invaluable in the study of living materials. Whether you use round or square cover slips will depend only on your own personal preferences. Cover slips are sold by the ounce, and an ounce should last quite a while.

Balance and Weights

There are some very inexpensive balance-and-weights sets now on the market. A balance suitable for home laboratory work should be accurate to at least one-tenth of a gram, and your weights should be calibrated in metric units (grams) rather than English units (ounces). A very adequate homemade balance is described later in this chapter, as is a set of homemade weights. Building these can save you several dollars.

Heaters

A Bunsen burner provides the best heat for most chemical experiments. If you have a convenient source of gas, you should certainly purchase an inexpensive burner of this type. And be sure to obtain a wing tip to fit it (for bending glass). As mentioned earlier, propane burners of the kind sold for home workshops can also be used. Their initial cost, however, poses a problem to those with very limited funds.

Less expensive, and most popular with home experimenters, are alcohol lamps. If you buy one, be sure it has a protective cap to fit over the wick when the lamp is not in use. But, as suggested later in this chapter, alcohol lamps are particularly easy to construct. You will probably want to make two or three for yourself. Small electric hot plates have many uses in laboratories of all kinds, but it is wise not to use one with an exposed heating element.

Electric Meters

Electric meters of various kinds are used in both physics and chemistry laboratories. Galvanometers detect and measure very small electric currents; ammeters measure larger electric currents; voltmeters measure electrical "pressure" (voltage). Both ammeters and voltmeters are of two kinds: direct current (d.c.) and alternating current (a.c.). Before purchasing any meters, it will be necessary for you to determine the probable ranges of a.c. or d.c. current and voltage you will encounter.

If you perform many experiments requiring the measurement of electrical quantities, you will soon learn how to modify most meters so that they can be used for ranges other than those indicated on their scales. Additionally, you might be able to afford a multimeter (an instrument combining several meters in one). It is sometimes possible to purchase fairly good meters rather inexpensively at government surplus stores.

Equipment You Can Make

There are two good reasons for making much of the equipment you will need for your experiments. First, scientific equipment may be very expensive. Second, you will learn much about the methods of science as you design and construct equipment especially tailored to your own particular work.

You will often find it possible to substitute simple homemade equipment for expensive commercial products by considering the specific purpose for which the equipment is to be used. For example, a costly string galvanometer is not needed to detect the presence of an electric current that is only moderately small. A coil of bell wire wrapped around a sensitive magnetic compass will do as well.

The following pages contain many ideas for constructing lab equipment. Most of the equipment described can be used in any laboratory, whatever the science being studied. Don't hesitate to make changes to suit your own requirements and available materials. Dimensions, when given, are intended to be only approximate.

Alcohol Burner

Most of your heating needs can be met with an alcohol burner such as that illustrated in Fig. 21. Use a widemouthed ink bottle that will not be easily upset. The wick can be either purchased or made by tying together a dozen or so strands of cotton yarn. Figure 22 shows how to make a wide-flame top for your burner. You will want this if you intend to bend glass tubing. The wide wick is of the type sold in hardware stores for use in kerosene lamps.

Denatured alcohol, obtainable from most hardware stores and drugstores, should be used to fuel your burner. Always keep the container tightly closed and away from excessive heat, and replace the cap over the wick after using your burner. This last measure will assure you that the burner is out (the flame can be nearly invisible under certain condi-

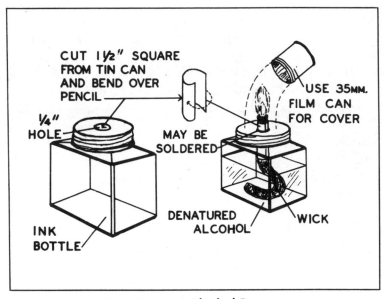

Fig. 21.   An Alcohol Burner

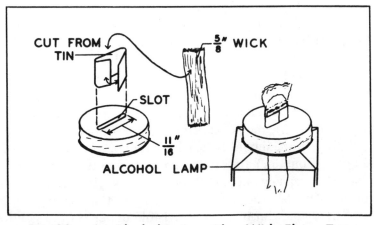

Fig. 22.   An Alcohol Lamp with a Wide-Flame Top

tions) and help prevent the alcohol from evaporating. If you desire, the metal cap shown in the sketch can be replaced by a 1-inch piece cut from the bottom of a broken test tube.

Electric Heater

The electric heater in Fig. 23 will be very useful in your lab. It is ideal for heating any material that might burn easily and for evaporating liquids. Use tin snips to do the cutting and a hand or electric drill to make the holes.

The socket can be taken from a discarded lamp or purchased at a hardware store. Be sure its base is equipped with a threaded tube and hexagonal nut, as shown. A porcelain socket can be substituted for the one illustrated, if desired. Such sockets are designed to be mounted with two bolts and nuts.

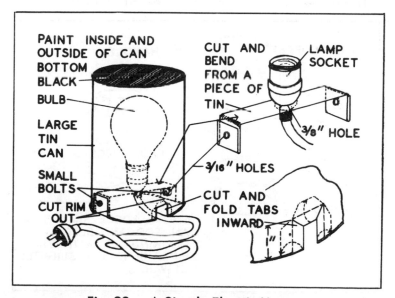

PAINT INSIDE AND OUTSIDE OF CAN BOTTOM BLACK

BULB

LARGE TIN CAN

SMALL BOLTS

CUT RIM OUT

CUT AND BEND FROM A PIECE OF TIN

LAMP SOCKET

3/8" HOLE

3/16" HOLES

CUT AND FOLD TABS INWARD

1"

Fig. 23. A Simple Electric Heater

Paint black the inside and outside of the can bottom (actually the top of the stove), and you will get more efficient heating. The amount of heat produced will also depend on the size bulb being used. Never use a unit larger than 75 watts; with that size, small amounts of water can be boiled in only a few minutes.

Drying and Sterilizing Oven

The oven in Fig. 24 can be used with the electric heater just described. It can also be set on a tripod and heated with an alcohol lamp. Note that the dish support merely stands on the lid of the coffee can; it is not attached. The lid is slotted with a pair of tin snips and is bent slightly outward. This is done so that the can will fit very loosely into the lid. There should be no sticking when it is removed.

To use the oven for drying, set the lid (now the bottom

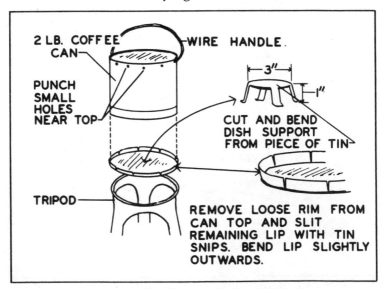

Fig. 24.   A Drying and Sterilizing Oven

of the unit) on the heater. Center the dish support on the lid, and place the container holding the material to be dried on the center of the support. Invert the can over the lid and turn on the heat. You can inspect the progress of the drying by lifting the can every half-hour or so. But be careful in doing this; the wire handle can become quite hot.

For sterilizing, place a metal jar lid full of water directly under the dish support. An electric-bulb heater, if used, should have a bulb large enough to boil the water. Place whatever is to be sterilized on the dish support, cover it with the can, and turn on the heat. Let the water boil for an hour before removing the can and disconnecting the heater. Although this sterilizer is not so effective as a commercial pressure unit, it will work well enough. Remember, when using it, that steam can produce very painful burns; keep your hands away from the openings.

Glassware

Various kinds of glassware are needed in any laboratory for heating, measuring, mixing, and otherwise handling various substances. Many suitable glass items can be found in your kitchen, local supermarket, or dime store.

Ordinary, clear water glasses can be used in place of beakers in experiments in which no heating is required. Heat-resistant custard dishes can be used for evaporating liquids and drying biological materials. Glass coasters have many uses in chemistry and biology experiments, and even discarded toy dishes can be of great value. Figure 25 shows how to make a graduated cylinder from a tall olive or bath-salts bottle. The baby bottle used to do the measuring should be graduated in cubic centimeters (cc.). You can buy one very cheaply in a drug- or dime store.

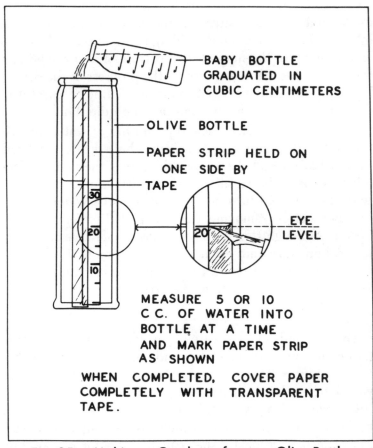

Fig. 25. Making a Graduate from an Olive Bottle

Test Tube Racks

If you are interested in chemistry, you will need several test tube racks of the kind illustrated in Fig. 26. Notice that, to help prevent upsetting, the base is almost as wide as the rack is tall. If you have difficulty drilling the partial holes in the base, don't give up. It's just as easy to drill the holes

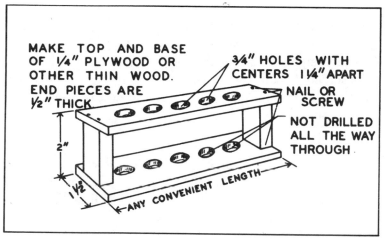

Fig. 26. A Wood Test Tube Rack

all the way through and fasten a piece of thin hardboard to the bottom.

A wire rack (Fig. 27) is ideal for holding large numbers of test tubes for certain kinds of biological experiments.

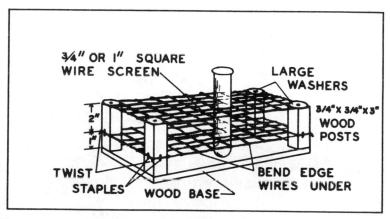

Fig. 27. A Wire Test Tube Rack

Galvanized screening of the type shown can be obtained from many hardware stores. Note that the corner posts are 3/4 inch square — about the same size as the mesh of the wire screen. Secure the outside wires of the screen by twisting them at the corners. Edge wires should be bent under with a pair of pliers.

Glassware Draining Rack

If you are interested in any science in which glassware is extensively used, you might want to provide yourself with a draining rack similar to that in Fig. 28. It will be very handy for drying many items at once. The one shown is intended to be mounted on a wall near the laboratory bench. The drain tray at the bottom will prevent excess water from running on the floor. Leave this tray unpainted, but line it with metal foil. Notice that the pegs in the upper row of

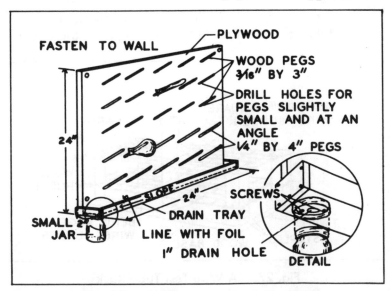

Fig. 28. A Glassware Draining Rack

the rack are smaller in diameter and shorter than those in the lower rows.

Supports and Clamps

The easiest support to make is the tripod shown in Fig. 29. Various sizes can be made by using cans of different heights and diameters. Note that a square of wire screen (or wire gauze) is placed over the tripod when glass containers are to be heated. Always use a wire screen in this manner regardless of the kind of support used. Never allow open flames to come in direct contact with glassware other than test tubes.

Figure 30 illustrates the construction of a ring stand and rings. Any small-diameter metal rod or pipe can be used for the stand. The extra block on the base should be drilled before it is cut to size; make the hole slightly smaller than the diameter of the pipe or rod. To assure a snug fit without

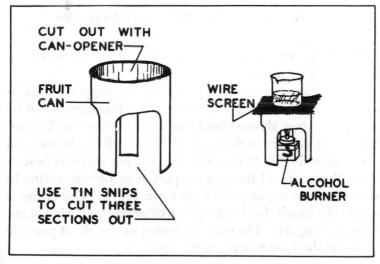

CUT OUT WITH CAN-OPENER

FRUIT CAN

WIRE SCREEN

USE TIN SNIPS TO CUT THREE SECTIONS OUT

ALCOHOL BURNER

Fig. 29. A Tin Can Tripod

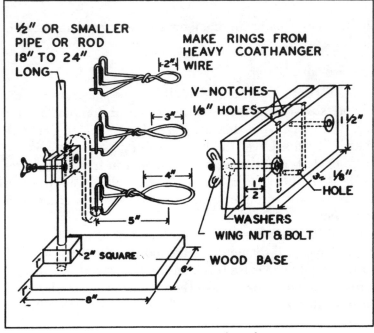

Fig. 30.   A Ring Stand and Rings

splitting the wood, cut a 2-inch slot in the bottom of the rod or pipe with a hacksaw.

Notice that the wood ring-and-clamp support block is drilled so that a variety of homemade attachments can be used. The rings shown should be bent so that the distance from their centers to the support block will be the same in every case. The bottom wires on the rings serve as braces. Bend them around the ring support arms before cutting to size. This also applies to the clamp in Fig. 31. The clamp is especially handy for holding test tubes on your ring stand (see also Fig. 51). The bolts and wing nuts make it possible to adjust the tube to any angle.

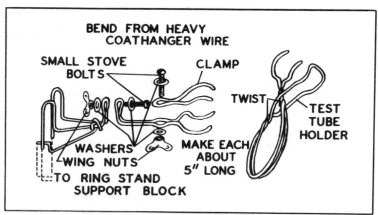

BEND FROM HEAVY
COATHANGER WIRE

SMALL STOVE
BOLTS

CLAMP

TWIST

TEST
TUBE
HOLDER

WASHERS

WING NUTS

TO RING STAND
SUPPORT BLOCK

MAKE EACH
ABOUT
5" LONG

Fig. 31.   A Clamp and Test Tube Holder

Although wire test-tube holders are cheap, it takes only
a few minutes to bend one from coat-hanger wire. One way
to do this is suggested in Fig. 31. When heating test tubes
held in a wire clamp or holder, be sure to support them near

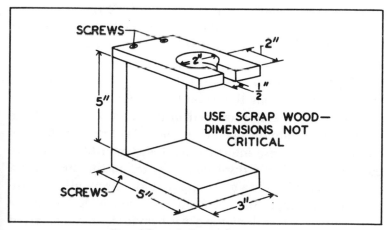

SCREWS

2"

2"

1/2"

5"

USE SCRAP WOOD—
DIMENSIONS NOT
CRITICAL

SCREWS

5"

3"

Fig. 32.   A Funnel Support

the top. Burner flames should not be allowed to touch the wire.

Funnels can be supported by a ring and ring stand, but a special support will be more convenient to use. The one shown in Fig. 32 can be constructed from scrap pieces of wood. If your funnel has a very long stem, merely use a longer vertical support for the stand.

Displacement Pan

A displacement pan (Fig. 33) is a standard piece of chemistry lab equipment. It is used to collect gases produced from various chemical reactions. Of course, such a pan won't work with gases that are extremely soluble in water (for example, ammonia).

To use the displacement pan illustrated, fill it with enough water to more than cover the tunafish-can bottle support. Then set the pan so that any overflow water will drip into your sink. Fill one or more wide-mouthed jars with water (use care, and you'll be able to actually "heap" the water up over the jar top). Finally, slide a small square of glass over each jar, make sure that there are no trapped air bubbles, and invert the jars in the pan. When ready to start collecting gas, carefully lift one of the bottles onto the tunafish can without allowing the water to run out.

After gas is being produced in the generator, insert the delivery tube into the opening in the side of the tunafish can so that bubbles rise into the inverted, water-filled jar. The gas will then slowly displace the water in the jar. After a jar is thus filled, slide a glass square under its mouth, remove it from the water, and set it on your bench. Keep the jar right side up if you think the gas is heavier than air, inverted if lighter than air. Repeat the process until you have filled all the jars or until the generator stops producing gas.

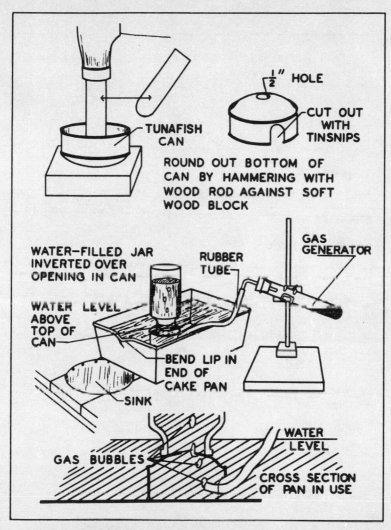

Fig. 33. Making a Displacement Pan to Collect Gases

Caution: If the gas generator used is being heated with a burner, remove the delivery tube from the displacement pan *before* removing the flame from the generator; other-

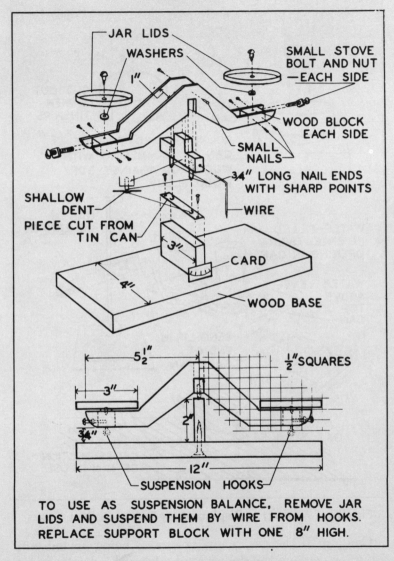

JAR LIDS

WASHERS

1"

SMALL STOVE
BOLT AND NUT
—EACH SIDE

WOOD BLOCK
EACH SIDE

SMALL
NAILS

¾" LONG NAIL ENDS
WITH SHARP POINTS

SHALLOW
DENT

PIECE CUT FROM
TIN CAN

WIRE

3"

CARD

4"

WOOD BASE

5½"

½" SQUARES

3"

2"

¾"

12"

SUSPENSION HOOKS

TO USE AS SUSPENSION BALANCE, REMOVE JAR
LIDS AND SUSPEND THEM BY WIRE FROM HOOKS.
REPLACE SUPPORT BLOCK WITH ONE 8" HIGH.

Fig. 34.   A Beam Balance

wise water might flow through the tube and fill the vacuum created in the cooling generator. If the gas being produced is inflammable or explosive when mixed with air, keep the heated generator as far from the displacement pan as the delivery tube will allow. Hydrogen generators do not require heat, but for safety's sake they should be wrapped with several layers of damp cloth before being used.

Balance and Weights

Construction details of two variations of a beam balance are shown in Figs. 34 and 35. The capacity of both types is about 200 grams. When used as indicated in Fig. 34, the balance is very sensitive to weight changes of less than one-tenth of a gram. But to achieve accuracy, both the object being weighed and the weights must be exactly centered on their pans. With suspended pans (Figs. 35, 47, and 48), the balance is slightly less "touchy" and is still capable of accuracy to about one-tenth of a gram. Note the stove bolts

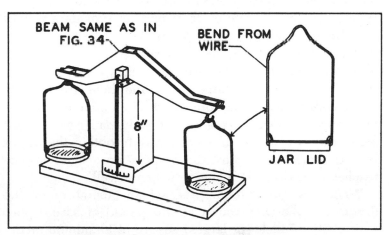

Fig. 35.   A Suspended-Pan Balance

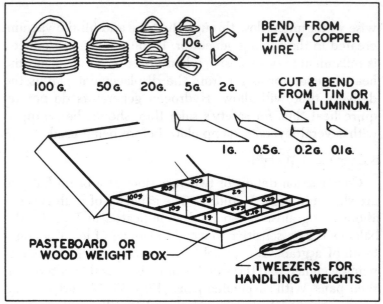

BEND FROM HEAVY COPPER WIRE

100 G. 50 G. 20 G. 5 G. 2 G. 10 G.

CUT & BEND FROM TIN OR ALUMINUM.

1 G. 0.5 G. 0.2 G. 0.1 G.

PASTEBOARD OR WOOD WEIGHT BOX

TWEEZERS FOR HANDLING WEIGHTS

Fig. 36. A Set of Homemade Weights

and nuts set into each side of the balance beam (on both types). The nuts rotate on their bolts to provide a weight adjustment for centering the beam.

If you construct one of these balances, you'll probably also want to make a set of weights. The weights shown in Figs. 36, 47, and 48 can be cut and bent from heavy scrap copper wire and thin sheet aluminum or tin. To make them, you will need a commercial balance and weight set to use as a standard. A good way to obtain the use of this equipment is to enlist the cooperation of your science teacher or a druggist whom you know well.

When you go to either the school laboratory or the drugstore, take with you at least a pound of bare copper wire, a 3-by-3-inch (or larger) square of aluminum or tin, a pair of pliers with wire cutter, a pair of tin snips, and a prepared weight box and tweezers, as shown in the illustrations. Always handle the borrowed weights (and your own finished ones) with the tweezers. Otherwise, oil and perspiration from your hands will spoil their accuracy. To make your weights, proceed as follows:

1. Place a 100-gram weight on the right-hand pan of the balance. Cut a length of wire that you think weighs more than 100 grams, fold it, and place it on the left pan. If this pan does not swing down, the wire was not long enough; so try again with a longer piece. When you have found the proper length, carefully snip small pieces from the wire until it exactly balances the 100-gram weight. Start again with a fresh piece of wire if you overcut.

2. Straighten out the 100-gram length of wire and cut other wires slightly more than one-half, one-fifth (two needed), and one-tenth its length. Use these wires to repeat the above procedure with 50-gram, 20-gram, and 10-gram weights, respectively, on the right-hand pan.

3. Cut wires slightly more than one-fifth (two needed) and one-half the length of the completed 10-gram weight. Trim these to exact size with 2- and 5-gram weights, respectively, on the right-hand pan.

4. Cut the square of aluminum or tin in half and place one of the halves on the left-hand of the balance. Place a 1-gram weight on the right-hand pan. (or move the balance's sliding weight to 1 gram). Use the tin snips to trim small pieces from the metal until it weighs exactly 1 gram. From the other half of the square, and in similar fashion, make weights of 0.5 gram, 0.2 gram (two needed), and 0.1 gram.

5. Recheck each one of the weights you have made

against the known weights, and then bend them as shown in Fig. 6. The wire can be formed around any small rod or pipe. Notice that one end of the longer wires is bent to make a hook. The short wires, too, have been bent into shapes that are easy to handle with tweezers. And one corner of each of the sheet-metal weights is turned up. As each of the weights is completed, it should be put into the proper compartment in the box. When finished, you should have the following gram weights: one 100-gram, one 50-gram, two 20-gram, one 10-gram, one 5-gram, two 2-gram, one 1-gram, one 0.5-gram, two 0.2-gram, one 0.1-gram. This combination of weights will permit you to weigh items up to 200 grams in steps of one-tenth of a gram.

Get into the habit of using proper procedures whenever you weigh anything on either a homemade or a purchased balance. The following simple rules are standard:

1. Weights are always placed on the right-hand pan of the balance.
2. Objects being weighed are always placed on the left-hand pan of the balance.
3. When weighing anything, always start with the largest weight that will not cause the pan to swing down. Then, add the next largest weight. If this causes the pan to swing down, remove the weight and replace it with the next size smaller. Repeat this procedure until the addition of the very smallest weight causes the pan to swing down. The weight of the object will then be the total of the weights in the pan.
4. Always replace weights in their proper compartments immediately after removal from the balance.

5. Never pour chemicals directly onto a weighing pan. Put a square of paper on the pan first (see Chapter 4).

Incubator

Many kinds of biological specimens and cultures are best grown in a heated incubator. The one shown in Fig. 37 is easy to construct and works well. The size, as always, will depend on your particular needs. With a little ingenuity, you can connect a discarded oven or furnace thermostat in series with the electric bulb. This will allow you to maintain very constant temperatures. The incubator will be dark inside unless you cut off the bottom of the can that surrounds the bulb.

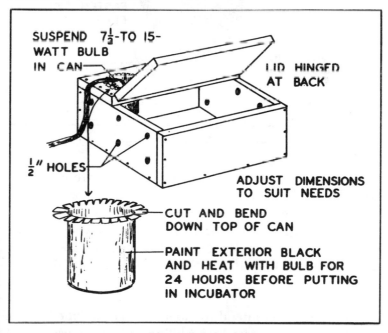

SUSPEND $7\frac{1}{2}$-TO 15-WATT BULB IN CAN

LID HINGED AT BACK

$\frac{1}{2}''$ HOLES

ADJUST DIMENSIONS TO SUIT NEEDS

CUT AND BEND DOWN TOP OF CAN

PAINT EXTERIOR BLACK AND HEAT WITH BULB FOR 24 HOURS BEFORE PUTTING IN INCUBATOR

Fig. 37. An Incubator

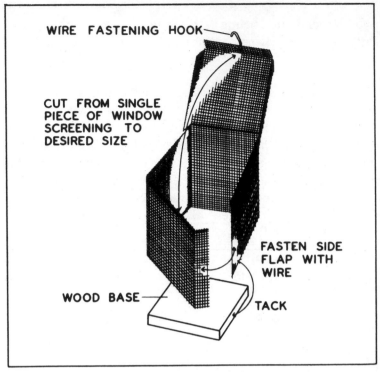

Fig. 38. An Insect Cage

Insect Cage

Glass jars do not provide an adequate environment for live insects. The cage illustrated in Fig. 38 is more suitable and can be made in a variety of sizes. When using it, put in some twigs and leaves from plants on which you have observed the insect under study. A small jar of water placed in the cage will keep the leaves green for several days.

Insect Killing Jar

Insects that you intend to mount should be killed at the time they are collected. Insect killing jars of the usual kind

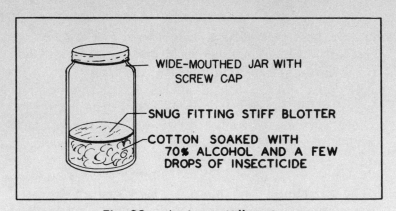

Fig. 39.   An Insect Killing Jar

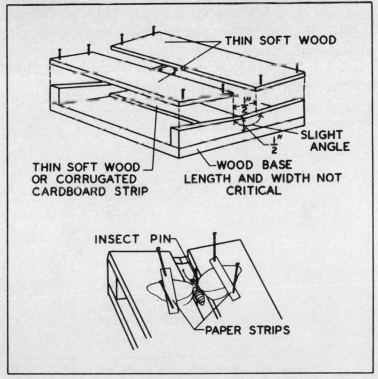

Fig. 40.   An Insect Spreading Board

must not be kept around a home laboratory, however, because of possible danger to small children. You will find the jar shown in Fig. 39 to be quite satisfactory, except for small green insects such as aphids. Carry three or four sizes of these jars with you on collecting trips; struggling insects will damage each other if they are overcrowded. Specimens must be kept in the jars at least 24 hours.

Insect Spreading Board

The spreading board shown in Fig. 40 will prove useful in preparing winged insects for display. Its top surfaces are made of very soft wood for ease in inserting pins. Instructions for using this board will be found in the next chapter. Winged insects awaiting mounting can be conveniently filed in corners cut from old envelopes, as indicated in Fig. 41. Notice that key information has been written on the upper part of the envelope corner.

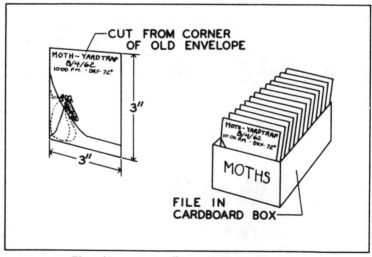

Fig. 41.   Butterfly and Moth Storage

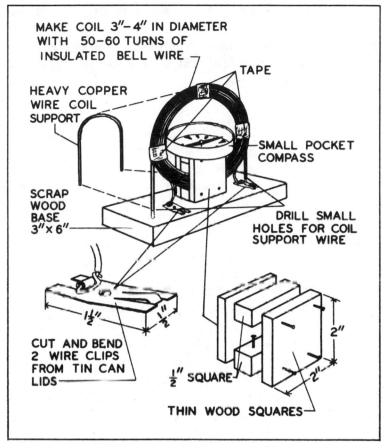

MAKE COIL 3"–4" IN DIAMETER
WITH 50–60 TURNS OF
INSULATED BELL WIRE

TAPE

HEAVY COPPER
WIRE COIL
SUPPORT

SMALL POCKET
COMPASS

SCRAP
WOOD
BASE
3"× 6"

DRILL SMALL
HOLES FOR COIL
SUPPORT WIRE

CUT AND BEND
2 WIRE CLIPS
FROM TIN CAN
LIDS

1½"

½"

½" SQUARE

2"

2"

THIN WOOD SQUARES

Fig. 42.   A Simple Galvanometer

Simple Galvanometer

The galvanometer illustrated in Fig. 42 can be used to detect small electric currents. Its dimensions should be adjusted to suit the compass available, and the compass need not be fastened to the support block. To use this galvanometer, face it so that the compass needle points directly to the coil of wire. When a current of electricity passes through the coil, it will then cause the needle to be deflected to one side.

Materials

While equipment is used over and over again, often in many different experimental situations, materials are used up and have to be replenished periodically. There are many thousands of kinds of materials that are of use in the home laboratory; it's not possible even to begin to list them all. Chemicals, however, are one of the more important items in this category.

Chemicals

Uncommon, or very pure, substances are usually purchased from chemical or laboratory supply companies. Drugstores, on the other hand, stock quite a few of the chemicals most needed in a home laboratory. Other chemicals can be purchased in large grocery stores, under a variety of trade names. Chemical substances are sold in a number of degrees of purity and, generally speaking, highly pure chemicals cost much more than commercial types. It is not economical to pay for higher purity than will be needed for a particular purpose.

Chemically pure (C.P.) or analytical-grade chemicals are the purest and most expensive. These are needed only for experiments where certain kinds of impurities would interfere greatly with the outcome. United States Pharmacopoeia (U.S.P.) chemicals have minor impurities, but are quite satisfactory for general laboratory use. Technical

(Tech.) or commercial-grade chemicals contain many impurities, some of which may not be listed on the label. These may be studied for their physical properties, used for producing other chemical substances, etc. Chemicals obtained from grocery and hardware stores are usually of the commercial grade.

When purchasing chemicals, be practical. Don't purchase a greater quantity of a substance than you will use over a reasonable period of time. On the other hand, some chemicals are so cheap (table salt or sugar, for example) that you will have to buy a relatively large amount if you want any at all. In this case, store only the amount you actually need in your laboratory and give the excess to your family.

The list of chemicals in Appendix A gives the common names of many substances. You can save yourself time and money by studying it carefully before setting out to buy chemicals. A word of caution, however: While it is true that you can sometimes purchase commercial grades of certain chemicals very cheaply under common or trade names, it may be possible to obtain others under their chemical names at even less cost. For instance, commercial-grade sodium hydroxide (available at any chemical supply house) costs much less per pound than does the same substance sold as a drain cleaner.

Other Materials

If you are studying chemistry, you'll discover that it isn't necessary to keep a large number of the compounds of each element on hand. Often substances can be substituted for, or made from, other chemicals. Physics, earth science, and space science laboratories require few chemicals, and these are rarely uncommon ones. Biological stains and solvents, for the most part, will have to be purchased from companies specializing in scientific supplies. Your needs in this area will be determined by your interests; consult a good microscopy handbook for specific recommendations.

Other materials you may need in your lab include filter and test papers, metal, wire, wire fasteners, and cement. Before purchasing these items, consider the exact purpose for which they are to be used. It is often possible to substitute inexpensive common materials, and even household discards, for costly special products. Don't make the mistake, however, of cluttering up your laboratory shelves with materials just because they are cheap or free. Never store anything for which you have no use.

CHAPTER 4

Procedures You Will Need to Know

With your laboratory all stocked and ready to use, it's time to discuss the techniques you must know in order to carry out your experiments. Remember that equipment, materials, and facilities are worthless unless used properly, and that many potentially good experiments have failed because the investigator was not aware of some important procedure. The techniques presented in this chapter are known to be those most needed by home experimenters. Master the ones necessary in your field, and you'll be well on your way to operating a successful lab.

Cutting and Bending Glass Tubing

Unlike most other kinds of laboratory glassware, tubing often must be cut and bent to particular sizes and shapes. Use soft glass tubing in any situation in which bending is required. It softens at a much lower temperature than the hard, or heat-resistant, variety. The latter will not bend even when heated to a dull red color.

Figure 43 illustrates the technique for cutting. Begin by

holding the piece to be cut firmly on the bench with your left hand. Press the edge of a triangular file against the tubing with your right hand, and draw the file back and

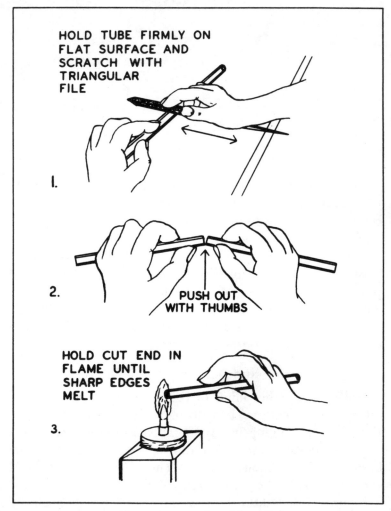

Fig. 43. How to Cut Glass Tubing

forth enough times to make a noticeable scratch. Next, hold the tube as shown and push outward with your thumbs. The tube should now break cleanly at the scratch. Note that if a small splinter of glass should be thrown out in the process, it would fly away from your face.

The cut ends of the tube will be quite sharp, so the next step is to fire-polish them. This is done by holding each end in the hot part of a burner flame until the glass becomes red and the sharp edges disappear. Then, set the tube on an asbestos pad to cool thoroughly. Glass can produce a painful burn long after it "looks" cool, and it's surprising how often even the most experienced people forget this.

To bend tubing, you will need a wide flame on your burner. A wing tip for spreading the flame of a gas burner can be purchased for a few cents, or bent from a piece of tin. Figure 22, as you will recall, shows how to make a wide flame top for an alcohol lamp.

Before heating the tube, decide where and how much you want to bend it. It's a big help to draw two straight lines at the desired angle on a piece of paper. These can be used as a guide for getting just the right bend.

Caution: Never allow a hot glass tube to touch the paper; hold the tube several inches above it.

Heat the tube slowly at first, turning it in the flame, as indicated in Fig. 44. Notice that the tube is being held in the hot upper portion of an alcohol flame. If you use a gas burner, adjust the air intake so that the flame is yellow. When the tube begins to turn a dull red and seems to flex as it is being turned, remove it from the flame, hold it over the guidelines, and quickly bend it to the proper angle. As always, lay the hot tube on an asbestos pad or other heat-

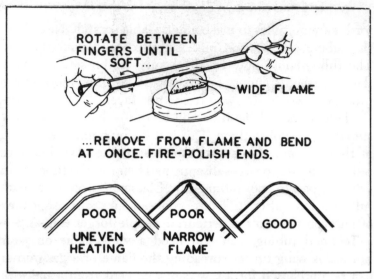

ROTATE BETWEEN
FINGERS UNTIL
SOFT...

WIDE FLAME

...REMOVE FROM FLAME AND BEND
AT ONCE. FIRE-POLISH ENDS.

POOR
UNEVEN
HEATING

POOR
NARROW
FLAME

GOOD

Fig. 44.　How to Bend Glass Tubing

resistant surface until it has cooled enough to be safely handled.

A good bend should look like the one shown at the lower right in the illustration. With practice, you should be able to obtain bends like this every time. The bend at the lower left is the kind usually produced by uneven heating of the tube, while the one in the center frequently results from using too narrow a flame. If the glass tube breaks or cracks just after you put it in the flame, you are heating it too quickly. Try warming up the tube first by waving it back and forth over the flame a few times while turning it rapidly between your fingers.

There are many occasions when a piece of glass tubing with a dropper tip may come in handy. To make a pair of such tips, heat the center of a piece of glass tubing as though you were going to bend it. When the glass becomes soft, remove it from the flame and immediately pull the two ends of the tubing apart (see Fig. 45). Cut the tubing at the places shown and fire-polish the ends as previously described.

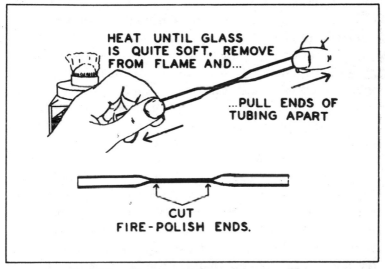

HEAT UNTIL GLASS IS QUITE SOFT, REMOVE FROM FLAME AND...

...PULL ENDS OF TUBING APART

CUT
FIRE-POLISH ENDS.

Fig. 45. How to Make a Dropper Tip

Be very careful with the fine glass tubing you remove from between the ends of the two dropper tips. If you don't intend to use it for an experiment, wrap it in several layers of newspaper and discard in the trash barrel. If saved, it should be put in a place where it will not accidentally puncture your fingers.

Connecting Glassware

Flasks, bottles, test tubes, condensers, and other pieces of glassware are connected by means of glass and rubber tubing, as Fig. 46 illustrates. Rubber stoppers are preferable to cork, but the latter type have the advantage of being easily bored to fit odd-sized glass tubing and are considerably cheaper. Corks should be bored with a sharp cork borer or hand drill. To assure an airtight fit, make the holes slightly smaller than the tubing.

Before trying to insert glass tubing in rubber or cork stoppers, moisten both the tubing and the stopper holes. Then hold the tube between your fingers and carefully twist it through the hole. Never force a tube or hold it so that it will pierce the hand if it breaks. When bent tubes are being inserted in stoppers, the bent portion should never be used as a lever. This will almost always cause the tube to snap. Finally, never try to insert glass tubes into stoppers while the stoppers are in place on containers.

Except in the case of a wash bottle (see Fig. 46) or other piece of permanent apparatus, do not leave glass tubing in rubber stoppers or tubes. In only a few days, the rubber will "cement" itself to the glass and it will be nearly impossible to take the joint apart without damage. Incidentally, try not to use stoppers that are too large or too small for their purpose. When a stopper is tightly inserted in the neck of a container, about one-third of it should be exposed.

Weighing Chemicals

Some general instructions for using a balance were given in the previous chapter, but it won't hurt to go into the procedure for weighing chemicals in a little more detail. Whether you use a homemade or commercial balance, you will find these techniques both economical of time and consistent in results.

To weigh out approximate amounts of solid chemicals, put a square of clean, smooth paper on the left pan of the balance, as shown in Fig. 47. This paper should be balanced

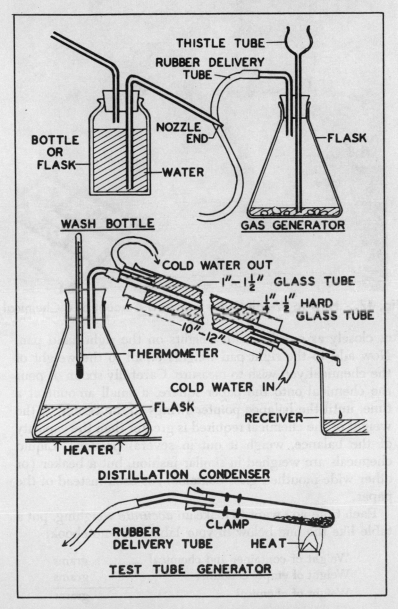

Fig. 46. Some Frequently Used Apparatus

Fig. 47.   How to Weigh Out a Required Amount of a Chemical

as closely as possible with weights on the right-hand pan. Now add to the right pan weights equal to the weight of the chemical you wish to measure. Carefully spoon or pour the chemical onto the paper square, a small amount at a time, until the balance pointer swings to the center. If the weight of the chemical required is greater than the capacity of the balance, weigh it out in several portions. Liquid chemicals are weighed in similar fashion, but a beaker (or other wide-mouthed glass container) is used instead of the paper.

Each time you want to make an *accurate* weighing, put a table like the one below in your laboratory notebook:

Weight of container and chemical	. . . . . . grams
Weight of empty container	. . . . . . grams
Weight of chemical	. . . . . . grams

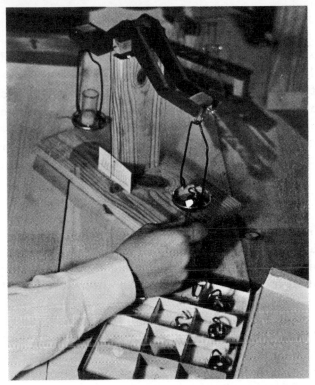

Fig. 48.   How to Find the Exact Weight of a Substance

A clean, dry glass container is used for accurate weighings of both solids and liquids. It should be placed on the left-hand pan of the balance and carefully weighed (empty) according to the procedure described in Chapter 3. Record its weight on the second line in your table. Now, put the chemical to be weighed into the container and weigh it again (see Fig. 48). This weight is recorded in the first line of your table. Subtract the second line from the first line to obtain the weight of the chemical.

After completing any weighing, be sure that all of the weights are returned to their proper places in the box. Also make certain that all traces of chemicals are removed from the left-hand pan of your balance.

At some time in the future, by the way, you will probably have occasion to use a glass-encased analytical balance. This balance resembles somewhat the balance shown in the photographs, but do not confuse the two. The weighing procedure for an analytical instrument has important differences from the techniques just described.

Measuring Volumes

Though you may have to weigh a liquid now and then, liquids are usually measured out by volume. Large amounts are measured with graduates, while burettes and pipettes are used for smaller amounts. The latter are illustrated in Fig. 49.

Burettes and pipettes are expensive to buy and impractical to construct, so you'll probably be doing most of your liquid measuring with graduates. Always use graduates of a size suitable for the work being done. In other words,

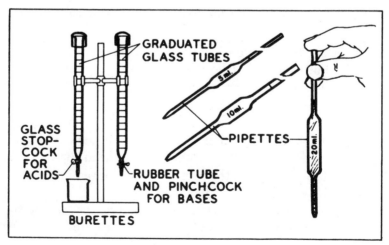

Fig. 49.   Burettes and Pipettes

don't try to measure out 1 milliliter of water with a 50-milliliter graduate. For estimating very small quantities of liquid, it is sometimes helpful to know that 10 drops of a water solution are approximately equal to 1 milliliter.

If you refer to Fig. 25, you will see how to read the scales of graduates and other equipment for measuring liquid volumes. Notice that the surface of the liquid shown has a downward curve. This will be true of most liquids, but a few will exhibit an upward curve. The curved portion of a liquid surface is called a *meniscus,* and the raised or depressed edge of the meniscus is ignored when reading a scale. The measuring scale on a graduate or similar piece of equipment should always be read with the eye perpendicular to it and level with the surface of the liquid.

Calculating and Preparing Solutions

A solution consists of two parts: the solvent and the solute. Solvents are usually common liquids, water being by far the most often used. When no solvent is mentioned, it is assumed to be water. Solutes are usually solids, but may also be liquids or gases, and are dissolved in the solvent. When one liquid is dissolved in another, it is sometimes not possible to say which is the solvent and which the solute. A 50 per cent by volume solution of alcohol and water is an example of this.

It is often important to know the amount of solute present in a given volume of a solution, and there are three common types of solutions for which this amount can be easily calculated. These are called *percentage, molar,* and *normal solutions.* Each variety has its own particular use.

You probably use water as a solvent in nearly all of the solutions you prepare. Since ordinary tap water usually contains enough impurities to interfere with many chemical reactions, distilled water should be used whenever possible. You can distill small amounts of water in your laboratory with the apparatus shown at the center of Fig. 46 (the thermometer will not be needed). In addition, frost scraped from the freezing compartment of a refrigerator is a source of fairly pure water.

Percentage Solutions

There are two ways to prepare and express percentage solutions: per cent of solute by volume, and per cent of solute by weight. Per cent by volume solutions are usually solutions of one liquid in another and are easy to make up. If you wish to prepare 100 milliliters of solution (this is always a convenient quantity), pour into a 100-milliliter graduate the number of milliliters of solute equal to the per cent solution desired. Then add sufficient solvent to make the total volume equal to 100 milliliters. For example, to prepare a 20 per cent by volume solution of alcohol in water, pour 20 milliliters of alcohol into a graduate and then add water until the 100-milliliter mark is reached.

Caution: Never prepare solutions of strong acids in water by the above method. The desired amount of water must be measured out first and poured into a heat-resistant glass container. Then measure out the volume of acid needed and *slowly* pour it into the water, while stirring constantly. Water poured into acid will spatter violently, getting all over your lab bench, clothes, and person.

Per cent by weight solutions are made up with the help of a scale or balance, and you will find it convenient to prepare 100 grams of solution at a time. Weigh out in grams an amount of solute equal to the desired per cent. Then subtract this number from 100 to obtain the weight of solvent required. Finally, dissolve the solute in the water to make a total of 100 grams of solution. For example, if you desire to prepare a 2 per cent by weight solution of sodium chloride (table salt), weigh out 2 grams of the salt and dissolve it in 98 grams of solvent.

Should the solvent be water, it is not necessary actually to weigh it out. Water at room temperature weighs just about 1 gram per milliliter, so merely measure out in milliliters the quantity of water equal to the number of grams required. Your measuring equipment will probably not be accurate enough to detect the very small error introduced by using this procedure.

If you know the percentage composition of a solution, you can always calculate the amount of solute present in any given amount. To do this, merely multiply the amount of solution by the per cent of solute and divide by 100. For example, 25 milliliters of a 40 per cent by volume solution of alcohol contains 25 × 40/100 (or 10) milliliters of alcohol. Fifteen grams of a 5 per cent by weight solution of sugar contains 15 × 5/100 (or 0.75) grams of sugar.

Molar Solutions

A molar solution is based on the molecular, or formula, weight of the compound used as the solute. This weight can be found by adding the atomic weights of all the atoms in a single molecule of the compound. The kinds and numbers of these atoms can be determined from the compound's chemical formula. The atomic weight of an element, incidentally, does not represent its actual weight. It tells us only how heavy the element is compared with other elements.

The list of common chemical compounds in Appendix A includes both chemical formulas and formula weights. Also in Appendix A are directions for calculating the formula weight of any compound for which you know the proper formula. Atomic weights will be found in Appendix B. It will be very helpful, in making up solutions, to include the formula weight of each compound on the label of its container.

A molar solution contains one formula weight of a compound taken in grams (or, a gram-formula weight) per liter of solution. Since 100 milliliters are one-tenth of a liter (1 liter = 1,000 ml.), 100 milliliters of a molar solution will contain one-tenth of a gram-formula weight of solute. Thus, to prepare 100 milliliters of a molar solution of a compound, dissolve one-tenth of a gram-formula weight of the solute in a small amount of water and then add sufficient water to produce 100 milliliters of solution.

Actually, it's usually not desirable to prepare molar solutions of many compounds. And in many cases, the required amount of solute will not even dissolve in the water. Fractional molar solutions, then, are more common. These are designated either by a decimal number written before the symbol M or by a fraction such as M/4 (one-fourth of a gram-formula weight of solute per liter of solution). A solution containing one-tenth of a gram-formula weight of solute per liter of solution can be designated as either 0.1 M or M/10.

For practice, prepare 100 milliliters of a 0.1 M solution of ordinary table sugar. If you turn to Appendix A, you will see that this compound has a formula weight of 342. One hundred milliliters of a molar solution would contain

342/10 or 34.2 grams of sugar. A 0.1 M solution will require one-tenth of this amount, or 3.42 grams of sugar. Weigh out 3.42 grams of sugar on your balance (or 3.4 grams if your balance is accurate to only one-tenth of a gram) and dissolve this in 50 or 60 milliliters of water. Pour the solution into a graduate and add more water until the volume is exactly 100 milliliters.

If you know the molarity of a solution, you can easily calculate the weight of solute present in any given volume. Remember that one liter (1,000 ml.) of a molar solution contains one gram-formula weight of solute. A liter of a fractional molar solution contains that fractional part of a gram-formula weight of solute. Thus, to find the amount of solute present in any volume of solution, divide that volume (in milliliters) by 1,000, multiply the quotient by the formula weight of the solute, and finally multiply this product by the decimal or fraction indicating the molarity of the solution. For example, 25 milliliters of a 0.1 sugar solution contain $25/1000 \times 342 \times 0.1 = 0.855$ grams of sugar. Since most of your measurements have been made accurate to only the first decimal place, this result should be rounded off to 0.9 grams of sugar.

Normal Solutions

Normal solutions are more commonly used by scientists than any of the other kinds. Although they are similar to molar solutions in some respects, normal solutions are based on a more sophisticated understanding of the structure and reactions of chemical compounds. For this reason, no attempt will be made here to explain the theoretical bases for normal solutions. It is enough to say that equal quantities of reacting solutions having the same normality will completely react with no leftovers.

If you work with normal solutions, you will find it convenient to study and remember the following relationship:

$$\text{Volume of solution required} = \frac{\text{Volume of reacting solution} \times \text{Volume of reacting solution}}{\text{Normality of required solution}}$$

This relationship states that if you desire to know how much of one solution will be needed to react exactly with a given volume of another, and if the normalities of both solutions are known, multiply the given volume of solution by its normality and divide the product by the normality of the solution whose volume you are seeking.

Suppose you desire to prepare some silver chloride by the reaction:

$$NaCl + AgNO_3 \longrightarrow NaNO_3 + AgCl \downarrow$$

or

Sodium chloride reacts with silver nitrate to produce sodium nitrate and a precipitate of silver chloride.

Let's say that you have already made up a 0.1 N solution of sodium chloride and a 0.05 N solution of silver nitrate and, the latter substance being fairly expensive, you decide to use only 15 milliliters of the solution. From the above relationship, you will discover that you need:

$$\frac{15 \text{ ml.} (AgNO_3) \times 0.05 \text{ (normality of } AgNO_3 \text{ solution)}}{0.1 \text{ (normality of NaCl solution)}} = \begin{array}{c} 7.5 \text{ ml.} \\ \text{NaCl solution} \end{array}$$

Normal solutions are prepared in the same manner as molar solutions, except that equivalent weights, rather than formula weights, of compounds are used. The equivalent weight of a compound is either the same as its formula weight or some simple fractional part of it. For example, the equivalent and formula weights of sodium chloride (58.5) are the same. The formula weight of calcium chloride is 111, while its equivalent weight is half this (55.5). The table in Appendix A shows the equivalent weights of compounds in parentheses after their formula weights.

Notice that equivalent weights are not given in all cases. They have not been given because equivalent weights are used for only certain classes of compounds. You should prepare percentage or molar solutions of compounds for which equivalent weights are not listed. In general, normal solutions of acids, bases (soluble hydroxides), and salts (compounds resulting from the reactions between acids and bases) are useful.

Filtering

There will be many occasions when you will want to remove solids suspended in liquid mixtures. Filtering is the usual method by which this is accomplished.

To filter, you will need a funnel, a funnel support (see Fig. 32), a beaker or other wide-mouthed glass container, a glass rod, and filter paper. Laboratory filter paper is ordinarily sold in round disks of varying sizes, the most popular size being 11 centimeters in diameter. Ordinary papers, by the way, are usually coated with various chemical substances that make them highly undesirable for filtering purposes.

In addition to these items, get yourself a wash bottle like the one shown in Fig. 46. With it, you can squirt a fine stream of liquid from the nozzle by forcing air through the open tube with your mouth or a rubber bulb. If available, a Florence flask (1,000 ml. size) should be used rather than the bottle illustrated.

The sketch at the bottom of Fig. 50 illustrates the steps to follow in folding your filter paper. After the paper is folded, insert it into the funnel and moisten with a little water from the wash bottle to hold it in place. If the liquid to be filtered is some solvent other than water, however, use that solvent to moisten the paper instead.

Arrange the funnel in its support as in Fig. 50, with the funnel tip just touching the side of the receiver. Pour the

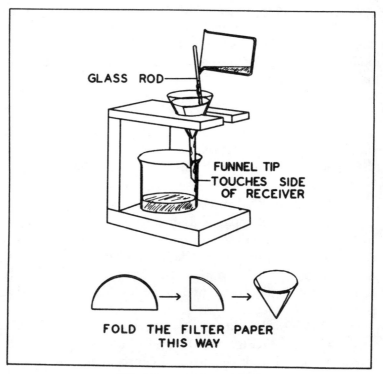

GLASS ROD

FUNNEL TIP
TOUCHES SIDE
OF RECEIVER

FOLD THE FILTER PAPER
THIS WAY

Fig. 50. How to Filter

liquid to be filtered down a glass rod, held at a slight angle. The bottom end of this rod should be below the top of the filter paper. Never allow the liquid in the funnel to rise above the top of the filter paper, and be very careful not to punch a hole in the bottom of the paper with the rod.

Filtering sometimes takes a long while, and you must be patient. But after most of the liquid has drained from the funnel, replace the receiver and rinse the residue (the solid left behind on the filter paper) several times. Use water (or whatever solvent is appropriate) from the wash bottle.

The residue can be taken from the filter paper by carefully scraping it off. It can also be removed by puncturing the bottom of the paper while it is still in the funnel and rinsing the solid into a clean receiver (use solvent from the wash bottle). In either case, the residue can be dried by evaporating away the solvent.

Heating Laboratory Glassware

Test tubes are the only glass containers you will ordinarily heat by direct contact with a flame. A tube might break, however, if its wire clamp or holder gets too hot. Clamps or holders should always be placed near the top of the test tubes, as indicated in Fig. 51. In this way, they will be as far from the flame as possible.

Test tubes are not usually held or supported in a vertical position while being heated. When in this position, boiling liquids or expanding gases can easily cause the contents of the tube to gush out. The tube in Fig. 51 is being supported at about the right angle for most purposes.

Start heating a test tube gradually, never holding the flame at any one point for very long. Notice how the burner in Fig. 52 is being held considerably below the portion of

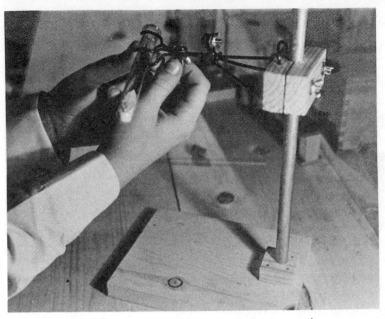

Fig. 51. How to Hold a Test Tube in a Clamp

the tube containing the chemical. Later, as the tube heats up, the burner will be brought in closer.

Open flames should never come in contact with the bottoms or sides of beakers and flasks. Such glassware should always be heated through a wire gauze or screen, as shown in Fig. 29. A square of wire gauze with an asbestos center is best for the purpose and costs little. If you use ordinary window screening, cut it into 5-inch squares. But be sure you don't get plastic screen material by mistake — the results can be dramatic, if not disastrous.

Collecting and Handling Biological Specimens

The following procedures for the collection, preservation, and storage of biological specimens are intended to help you

Fig. 52. How to Heat a Test Tube

get started in the laboratory study of biology. They are not necessarily the best or the most complete techniques you can use, and you will improve on them as you gain in knowledge and experience.

Small plant and animal specimens collected from ponds, lakes, etc. are best kept in containers holding some of the original water. In most cases, they will remain alive for several days with no further precautions. If you desire to separate particular specimens for detailed study, place them in jars containing more of the original water. Don't

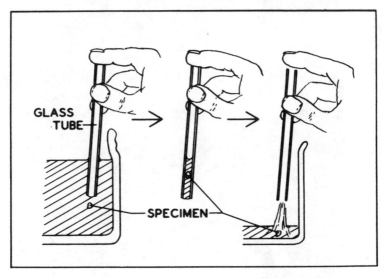

Fig. 53.   How to Transfer a Small Specimen

use tap water unless it has first been allowed to stand uncovered for several days. Tap water, of course, should *never* be used for specimens that have been taken from the sea.

Figure 53 shows how a glass tube can be used to transfer very small (but not microscopic) plant or animal specimens from one container to another. Be sure to label all specimen containers with the source, date of collection, and other useful information.

Insects should not be removed from killing jars for at least 24 hours. After this time, small beetles and flies can be temporarily stored in small, dry glass jars. Butterflies and moths can be kept in old envelope corners, as previously described.

But insects that have been stored for more than a day or

two are usually too brittle to mount. To soften, place them on a moist piece of blotting paper in a covered plastic or glass dish for at least a day. Put a drop of any common antiseptic solution (for example, dilute phenol) on one corner of the blotting paper. This will help to prevent the growth of mold.

Winged insects are prepared for display on a spreading board like that shown in Fig 40. The pin through the center of the thorax (body) should be a black insect-mounting pin. Such pins are available in three sizes from most scientific supply firms. Notice that in the illustration the wings are spread out and held in place by strips of paper. Before spreading, however, use tweezers to stretch out the legs and antennae into proper position. Allow insects to remain on the spreading board for two or three days before placing them in a display case or tray.

Beetles and flies need not be dried on a spreading board. Merely mount them on pins, straighten their legs with tweezers, and stick the pins in a soft board or piece of corrugated cardboard. Unlike other insects, incidentally, beetles should not be pinned through the center of the thorax. Pin them to one side of the center.

Observing Living Specimens through the Microscope

There are many techniques for preparing various kinds of microscope slides. You will learn about some of these from any good microscopy handbook, and you may even invent a few of your own. Until then, however, you will enjoy using the technique illustrated in Fig. 54 for making slides of live specimens.

Prepare a slide by cementing to it a thick fiber or nylon washer with an opening at least one-quarter inch in dia-

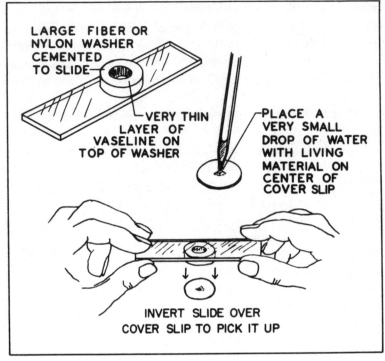

Fig. 54. A Hanging Drop Slide

meter. You can use model-airplane cement (not the plastic variety) or clear fingernail polish, but keep the cement from spreading into the center opening. Next, apply a small amount of Vaseline around the top of the washer. (Again, be careful not to get any into the center opening.)

To use the slide, place a very small drop of water containing the living material onto the center of a cover slip. Carefully invert the slide over this drop so that the drop does not touch the side of the washer. The cover slip will adhere to the Vaseline and, if you carefully turn the slide right side up, the drop of water will be suspended from the cover slip. Now set the slide on a horizontal microscope stage. Because the drop is effectively sealed from the outside air, it will not evaporate for a long time. You can observe your specimens, therefore, without fear of their drying out.

It's a simple matter to slide the cover slip off the washer when you are through with a particular sample. Vaseline can be removed by dipping the glass in a small jar of cleaning or lighter fluid, then wiping it with a small bit of cotton or tissue. Store the modified slide carefully; you'll undoubtedly be using it again.

Measuring Time

The most common way to measure short periods of time is with a stop watch.Stop watches, unfortunately, are far from inexpensive, but you can make an ingenious substitute from an old record turntable. A 78 r.p.m. unit will work best, though slower speed can be also used.

First, using an old record as a pattern, trace and cut out a 10- or 12-inch disk from heavy cardboard. Cut a spindle hole as close to the exact center as possible, paint the disk with black or dark-colored enamel, and let it dry. Now lightly sprinkle bath powder or chalk dust over the surface and place your disk on the turntable.

When you are about to time something, switch on the turntable motor and hold a broom straw (or a long flexible sliver of wood) an inch or so above the edge of the disk. At the instant you want to start timing, lower the straw against the surface of the disk and slowly move it toward the center spindle. With practice, this motion can be stretched out for as long as a minute, if necessary. At the instant you want to stop timing, lift the straw away, switch off the motor, and remove the disk.

From the outside starting point of the long spiral traced by the straw, carefully trace a line straight to the center hole. Count the number of times the spiral has intersected this line and add the fractional part of a turn (estimated) made by the very last portion of the spiral. To get the time, multiply this number by 0.769, the part of a second required for one complete turn of a 78 r.p.m. turntable. For a 45 r.p.m. machine, multiply by 1.333 seconds; for a 33⅓ r.p.m. machine, 1.80 seconds.

One way to make rough estimates of time is to use your pulse. Time your pulse as follows: stand near a clock with a sweep second hand; when the hand passes the 12-o'clock position on the dial, start counting beats. Stop counting after exactly 3 minutes and divide the number of elapsed seconds (180) by the number of beats. The quotient, a number representing the time per beat, should be recorded permanently.

In order to use your pulse to time something, merely count the number of elapsed beats and multiply by this number. Of course, you should not use such a method at times when your pulse is not beating at normal speed (when you are excited, for example).

CHAPTER 5

Some Ideas to Get You Started

By now you are probably quite eager to put your mind and your laboratory to work on a scientific investigation. The purpose of this chapter is to list some problems that might be suitable for study in a home lab, together with suggestions for working out ways to solve them. Just about every field of science is represented, and you should certainly find something intriguing. But first you must have a good understanding of how to plan an experiment.

Scientists conduct experiments in order to find answers to questions related to the problems they are studying. As a beginning scientist, you should do the same, for only in this way will your experiments be really meaningful. Of course, you will soon discover that it is not always easy to ask the right question. Sometimes you will think of many before you find one that can be properly tested by an experiment. But this is the essence of science, and the truly great scientists are the men who know how to ask the very best questions.

Actually, scientists ask their questions in an indirect manner. They think of a possible answer to a problem, and then write it down in the form of a statement of fact. Next, they design an experiment to test the truth of the statement. Frequently it is found to be untrue and rejected as a possible answer to the problem. At other times the experimental results merely indicate that the statement *might* be true, but should be tested further. This means that new ways must be found to express the statement so that better tests can be made. Rarely does a single experiment show a statement to be completely true.

The statements of possible answers to problems are called *hypotheses*. An example of a very simple one is the statement: air exhaled from the lungs contains a greater quantity of carbon dioxide than does ordinary air. Can you think of a way to test it?

Maybe you remember from your school science class that limewater turns cloudy when carbon dioxide is bubbled through it. After thinking about this for a moment, you might decide that one way to test the hypothesis would be to bubble equal volumes of ordinary air and exhaled air through equal volumes of limewater. If the hypothesis is true, the limewater through which the exhaled air is bubbled might turn cloudier than that through which the ordinary air is bubbled. On the other hand, there might be no apparent difference between the two samples of limewater. This could mean that the difference in amounts of carbon dioxide is too small to detect by the method tried. You would then want to test the hypothesis by some other experiment.

As you begin to work in your laboratory, always try to think of hypotheses to test. It is a good idea to write these down in your laboratory notebook for future reference. After you design and carry out experiments to test these hypotheses, record the details of the experimental procedure as well as the results. As you do this, you will discover the need to think of and test alternative hypotheses. Even the simplest problem can lead to a long chain of experiments, each one following from the test of a preceding hypothesis. This is the way the scientist proceeds from the known to the unknown.

The problems suggested below are intended to get you started on the roads to discovery. Some roads will be short, some long; and some will have most interesting detours. Remember, however, that what you discover will depend on how well you work out suitable answers to the problems and how well you design experiments to test the answers.

Some Things to Explore in Chemistry

How are metals different from nonmetals? There are literally hundreds of hypotheses that can be tested to help answer this problem. And one thing you should keep in mind is that there are both physical and chemical differences between the two classes of substances. You will probably find it easier to study one metal at a time, then compare your notes after studying several.

How can acids and bases be distinguished from other classes of compounds? As you study this problem, you will learn about the special properties of acids and bases and about chemical indicators. As a starter, assume that white vinegar contains an acid and limewater contains a base. Test the hypothesis that grape juice has one color when mixed with an acid and another when mixed with a base.

How small are molecules? This is a really fascinating problem. To begin your study, you might dissolve a few crystals of potassium permanganate in a small amount of water and make the hypothesis that 1 cubic centimeter of the resulting solution (a deep purple in color) contains at least one million molecules. To test this hypothesis, add one cubic centimeter of the solution to 999 cubic centimeters of water. Mix well, take out a cubic centimeter of the new solution, and add it to another 999 cubic centimeters of water. One cubic centimeter of this last solution (after a thorough mixing) contains one-millionth of the original cubic centimeter of solution. If you can still observe the color of the potassium permanganate, then the hypothesis might be a correct one.

What is the composition of water? Of any compound? This is not a simple problem, so don't be satisfied with testing the very first hypothesis that comes to mind. You probably already know that water is composed of hydrogen and oxygen. But do you know how the atoms of these elements are joined or what the shape of the water molecule might be? The second part of this problem can't be completely solved by any one person in a lifetime. As you will find, many other substances are less complicated.

What makes iron rust? Don't jump to hasty conclusions regarding this problem. If you tackle it, you might be due for some interesting surprises. As a clue to working out possible hypotheses, take a flat strip of uncoated iron and give it a high polish. Then make several scratches on it with a piece of sharp steel. Place the iron strip in a shallow container with a few drops of water, and cover the container with a transparent lid. The strip should be observed every half-hour or so. Pay close attention to the scratches.

What is the relation between the amount of solute in a solution and the freezing and boiling points of the solution? When you test various hypotheses connected with this problem, be sure to try a number of different kinds of compounds. For example, use sodium chloride, magnesium sulfate, table sugar, and calcium chloride. After you have obtained some measurements, see if there is any relation between them and the formula weights of the compounds.

Is there any relation between the colors of compounds and their component elements? As a starter, you might want to test the two similar hypotheses: "Blue compounds are copper compounds," and "Copper compounds are blue." Don't be hasty in drawing conclusions from just a few observations.

Why do some substances burn and others not? This is another problem that can give you some real surprises. Before you set up any hypotheses to test, make some oxygen by adding water to a small amount of sodium peroxide in a flask gas generator (see Fig. 46). Collect the gas in a wide-mouthed bottle (use a displacement pan). Carefully pour about 1/2 inch of dry sand into the bottom of the bottle, allowing as little of the gas to escape as possible. Then heat a bean-sized ball of fine steel wool in a flame until it is red hot. Using a pair of tongs, plunge the red-hot steel wool into the bottle of oxygen. The result of this little demonstration should suggest to you that the ability to burn may involve more than a chemical property.

How can small amounts of various chemical substances be identified? This problem, of course, is concerned with chemical analysis. In testing possible hypotheses, you will be searching for special chemical reactions, physical properties, and other patterns characteristic only of the substance being studied. Begin your study by heating a little starch in water and adding a drop of iodine solution (tincture of iodine). Then see if you can find any other substance that will produce the same color with starch.

What are the essential chemical components of an electric cell? You probably will need a galvanometer to help in the study of this problem. One of the hypotheses you should test is: in order for an electric current to be produced, one of the cell electrodes must react chemically with the electrolyte (cell liquid).

Some Things to Explore in Biology

How can various types of plants be distinguished from one another? This is a problem in classification. There are some obvious similarities among certain kinds of plants, while other groups are obviously different. Keep in mind, however, that the real differences among plants are not necessarily the obvious ones. Dandelions and pine trees, for example, are more closely related than they seem. Before you get very far with this problem, you will probably be using a microscope and planting seeds.

Are microscopic one-celled organisms sensitive to changes in temperature? Hypotheses regarding this problem can be relatively simple after you decide what to look for as evidence of sensitivity. The design of suitable experiments, however, will require some ingenuity on your part.

How does a particular kind of living organism adjust to changes in its environment? This can be a very interesting laboratory problem, regardless of what organism you study. In order to tackle various hypotheses, you will have to learn how to set up very carefully controlled experiments. If you don't, the adjustments you observe might not really be caused by the changes you have made in the organism's environment.

How fast can worms move through the soil? This rather amusing problem actually has some practical applications. It is also typical of a large number of investigations, related to the mobility of living organisms, which can be studied in a home laboratory. There is room for a high degree of originality in designing experiments.

How does moisture get up from the soil to the leaves of plants? Don't expect to have an easy time with this one. Even professional scientists are not quite sure of the answer yet. And you shouldn't hesitate to test such silly hypotheses as: Plants pull water up from their roots, as though the substance were wire or string. You might be surprised by the results.

How effective are certain insecticides against successive generations of a particular insect species? A study of this problem can make a very good science fair project. Experiments will have to be carried out over a period of several months, and you should use insects with short breeding periods. Several large insect cages will probably be needed.

What effect does (name of chemical) *have on the growth of* (name of plant)? Fill in the two blanks for whatever variation of this problem you want to study. You will need two sets of plants for your experiments. One group will be used as a control and will be treated exactly as the experimental group, except that the chemical will not be used. Any changes in the experimental group that are not observed in the control group can then be attributed to the presence of the chemical.

What insects are found in my neighborhood? An interesting variation of this observational problem is to make a study of the insects found in your neighborhood during particular months, seasons, or temperature ranges.

How much can (name of organism) *learn?* This can be a particularly intriguing problem if you substitute the name of a microscopic one-celled organism for the blank. Since the problem calls for some kind of measurement, you will have to develop a behavior scale against which to rate the performance of the organism.

How do the various parts of a plant differ chemically? You will find it useful to learn more about chromatography before you tackle this problem. And if you haven't done the chromatography experiment suggested in the introduction, you should try it. There are also some special precautions to be taken. For one thing, the chemical composition of any living organism cannot be expected to be exactly the same at various stages of growth. For another, a plant begins to die after it has been removed from the soil, and chemical reactions can be expected to produce materials not ordinarily found in the soil.

How can groups of living organisms be kept alive in a closed environmental system? This is a problem of particular importance to those concerned with space travel. Information regarding various kinds of closed environmental systems can be found in many scientific magazines and books. When studying this problem, don't forget the importance of keeping accurate records of your observations.

Some Things to Explore in Physics

What is the strength of a magnetic field at various distances and directions from the poles of a magnet? This can be a very tricky problem. You will soon discover that whatever technique you use to detect or measure a magnetic field will tend to change that field. To begin with, however, set up a small iron bob (such as a small washer) suspended in a test tube by a thread. Use another thread, weighted with a piece of lead or copper, as a plumb line. You can then measure with a protractor how far the first thread is pulled from the vertical at various distances and directions from the magnet.

How are heat and temperature related? Before you assume that heat and temperature are the same, try this: Drop equal weights of iron nails, copper wire, lead sinkers, and ordinary stones into separate containers of water. Heat the water in these containers to boiling, so that the materials in each will be raised to the same temperature. While waiting for the water to boil, prepare four more containers (all identical) with equal quantities of cold water at equal temperatures. Now, remove the hot materials from the boiling water and drop them into separate containers of cold water. After a minute or two, measure the temperature of each of the cold water containers and compare them with the original temperature. On the basis of your observations, will you accept or reject the hypothesis that heat and temperature are the same?

What effect do certain transparent materials have on polarized light? There are many hypotheses with regard to this problem that can be tested in the home laboratory. You can get some ideas by pressing several overlapping strips of transparent tape onto a glass square and holding the square between two pieces of polarizing material (lenses from an old pair of polarizing sun glasses will do). Look through the pieces as you slowly rotate one of them.

How are sound waves reflected? You will enjoy studying this problem. To make waves visible, fasten a stiff wire to the clapper arm of an electric bell. Support the bell so that the end of the wire barely dips into one end of a shallow tray (perhaps an aluminum cookie sheet) of water. Shine a light on the tray from above and start the bell. Observe the waves as they strike the side of the tray. If they are produced too quickly, slow down the clapper arm by attaching a small weight to it.

What is the relation between the weight of a pendulum and its period of swing? You will discover several sources of experimental error in investigating this problem. If you are alert, however, these sources will suggest some new problems to be studied.

What is the relation between the relative velocity and pressure of a flowing gas? This problem has innumerable applications in such diverse fields as aviation and baseball. The third experiment described in the introduction should suggest a hypothesis or two to test further in the laboratory.

How can the mass of an object be measured? If you have read very much about science, you probably know that mass and weight are not the same. To help solve the problem, imagine how an astronaut, while in orbit around the Earth (and thus, in a weightless condition), might measure the mass of some object in his space capsule. You will find it interesting to try to design some experiments in which the astronaut's "gravity-free" condition can be approximated.

What is the effect of surface color on the absorption of heat? The information you gather from experiments related to this problem might have some interesting applications around your home. As a start, try painting stripes of various colored paints on one side of a piece of tin. The back of the tin should be coated with candle wax (colored wax will be easier to observe). Now expose the painted side of the tin to a source of heat, such as an electric light bulb. Behind which colors does the wax melt first?

Some Things to Explore in Earth Science

What is the water capacity of the soil in my neighborhood? Many factors determine the amount of water that a particular kind of soil can hold. A series of well-designed experiments can yield some very interesting and useful results.

What kinds of rocks are found in my neighborhood? As you study this problem, you will have to be careful to distinguish between rock native to your neighborhood and rock that has been brought in from other areas for such things as building and road construction. You will find it convenient to use a rock and mineral handbook to aid you in identifying your samples.

How are clouds formed? There are many possible hypotheses here, most of them capable of being tested in a home laboratory. To get started, put 1/4 inch or so of water in the bottom of a wide-mouthed jar. Next, with a length of wire, fasten a piece of rubber from a balloon tightly over the mouth of the jar. The jar should be allowed to stand for a half-hour or so. When the time is up, pinch the center of the rubber between the fingers and suddenly pull it out to reduce the pressure in the jar. Observe what happens.

How are craters formed? Obtain a straight candle at least 3/4 inch in diameter and 6 to 10 inches long. Bore a hole in a 6-inch square of wood, and support the square in a horizontal position about 1 foot above the top of your bench. Insert the candle in the hole (from underneath) so that its top is just even with the upper surface of the wood. Light the candle, and as it burns slowly push it up so that the wick just shows above the top of the wax. The candle should be twisted slightly every once in a while so that it will not become stuck to the board. Your observations of what happens can form the basis for further experiments on crater formation.

What causes a straight stream of water eventually to become crooked? Ever wonder why a small country brook makes hairpin curves and loops as it wanders across an open field? One experiment that might give you part of the answer is rather easy to set up. Arrange a thin layer of moist sand or clay on the bottom of a gently sloping tray. Then make a straight channel, about an inch wide, from the top of the tray to the bottom. Place a flat-bottomed stone (about 1/2 inch in diameter) at one side of the channel halfway up the tray. A stream of water should now be allowed to flow down the channel. Observe what happens at the point where the water passes the stone.

Some Things to Explore in Space Science

What is the relation between the velocity of a satellite and the radius of its orbit? Fasten a small weight to the end of a string, then thread the string through a spool. Holding the spool in your right hand and the free end of the string in your left, swing the weight in a vertical circle. While the weight is swinging around, slowly pull the free end of the string through the spool. As the string shortens, watch what happens to the velocity of the weight. Now see if you can design some experiments to measure the velocity of the weight for various lengths of string.

What is the relation between the magnifying power of a telescope and the focal length of its lenses? This is really a physics problem, but it is directly related to astronomy. Use a variety of different sizes and shapes of lenses to test possible answers to this problem. The results of your experiments can be helpful in planning a homemade telescope.

How can the velocity of a spaceship be measured? Before you tackle this problem, read about the "Doppler effect" in a physics book. Assume that you want to measure the velocity of the ship relative to the Earth.

How can a gyroscope be used to keep a rocket on course? This is essentially a problem in applied science or engineering. Start your research by learning something about the special properties of gyroscopes.

Can life exist in space? Some scientists think it possible that simple forms of life have reached the Earth from other parts of the universe. To study this problem yourself, you will have to figure out ways to simulate some of the conditions of outer space in your laboratory. Use simple one-celled plants and animals, or mold spores, as the subjects of your experiments.

How can harmful radiation be detected? Plans for simple electroscopes and cloud chambers can be found in many books and magazines. In addition to these radiation detectors, you will also want to experiment with the use of photographic films. The problem is one of great concern to many space scientists.

Once you have selected a problem to work on in your laboratory, you are really in business as an investigator. But remember that what you learn from this book can be only a beginning. You must always be alert for new sources of scientific information and ideas. It's important, too, that you not get discouraged when working on a tough problem. Every scientist has many more experimental failures than successes. And the personal satisfaction gained from a few real discoveries far outweighs the disappointments of many failures.

APPENDIX A

Some Common Chemical Compounds

A Note about Formula Weights. The formula weight of a compound is the sum of the atomic weights of all of the atoms in the compound's chemical formula. Thus, the formula weight of water is equal to the weights of two atoms of hydrogen ($2 \times 1 = 2$) plus the weight of one atom of oxygen (16), or a total of 18.

The formula weight of a substance such as aluminum sulfate $Al_2(SO_4)_3$ is found by adding the weights of two aluminum atoms ($2 \times 27 = 54$) and three SO_4 groups (the sum of 32 and [4×16] multiplied by $3 = 288$), or a total of 342. The formula weight of a substance such as $CuSO_4 \cdot 5H_2O$ includes the weight of the attached number of water molecules.

Chemical Name	Common Name	Chemical Formula	Formula Weight; Equivalent Weight (in Parentheses)*
Acetic acid	present in vinegar	$HC_2H_3O_2$	60 (60)
Ethanol	grain alcohol	C_2H_5OH	46
Aluminum chloride		$AlCl_3$	133.5 (44.5)
Aluminum sulfate		$Al_2(SO_4)_3$	342 (57)
Ammonia		NH_3	17
Ammonium chloride		NH_4Cl	53.5 (53.5)
Ammonium hydroxide	ammonia water	NH_4OH	35 (35)
Ammonium nitrate		NH_4NO_3	80 (80)
Ammonium sulfate		$(NH_4)_2SO_4$	132 (66)
Barium chloride		$BaCl_2$	208 (104)

*All values have been calculated with atomic weights accurate to the nearest unit. The weight used for chlorine (35.5), however, is accurate to the nearest tenth.

Appendix A (*continued*)

Chemical Name	Common Name	Chemical Formula	Formula Weight; Equivalent Weight (in Parentheses)*
Boric acid	boracic acid	H_3BO_3	62 (20.7)
Calcium carbide	carbide	CaC_2	64
Calcium carbonate	limestone, chalk	$CaCO_3$	100 (50)
Calcium chloride		$CaCl_2$	111 (55.5)
Calcium hydroxide	slaked lime	$Ca(OH)_2$	74 (37)
Calcium oxide	quicklime	CaO	56 (28)
Calcium sulfate	gypsum	$CaSO_4·2H_2O$	172 (86)
Carbon dioxide	carbonic acid	CO_2	44
Copper (II) sulfate	blue vitriol	$CuSO_4·5H_2O$	250 (125)
Hydrochloric acid	muriatic acid	HCl	36.5 (36.5)
Hydrogen peroxide		H_2O_2	34
Hydrogen sulfide		H_2S	34 (17)
Iron (II) sulfate	green vitriol, copperas	$FeSO_4·7H_2O$	278 (139)
Iron (III) chloride		$FeCl_3·6H_2O$	270.5 (135.3)
Iron (II) sulfide		FeS	88
Magnesium chloride		$MgCl_2$	95 (47.5)
Magnesium hydroxide	milk of magnesia	$Mg(OH)_2$	58 (29)
Magnesium sulfate	Epsom salts	$MgSO_4·7H_2O$	246 (123)
Manganese dioxide		MnO_2	87
Nitric acid		HNO_3	63 (63)
Potassium aluminum sulfate	alum	$KAl(SO_4)_2·12H_2O$	474 (237)
Potassium bromide		KBr	119 (119)
Potassium chlorate		$KClO_3$	122.5 (122.5)
Potassium chloride		KCl	74.5 (74.5)
Potassium chromate		K_2CrO_4	194 (97)
Potassium fluoride		KF	58 (58)
Potassium hydroxide	caustic potash, lye	KOH	56 (56)
Potassium iodide		KI	166 (166)
Potassium nitrate	saltpeter	KNO_3	101 (101)
Potassium permanganate		$KMnO_4$	158 (158)
Potassium phosphate		K_3PO_4	212 (70.7)

*All values have been calculated with atomic weights accurate to the nearest unit. The weight used for chlorine (35.5), however, is accurate to the nearest tenth.

Appendix A (*continued*)

Chemical Name	Common Name	Chemical Formula	Formula Weight; Equivalent Weight (in Parentheses)*
Potassium sulfate		K_2SO_4	174 (87)
Silicon dioxide	silica, sand	SiO_2	60
Silver nitrate	lunar caustic	$AgNO_3$	170 (170)
Sodium acetate		$NaC_2H_3O_2$	82 (82)
Sodium bicarbonate	baking soda	$NaHCO_3$	84 (42)
Sodium bisulfate		$NaHSO_4$	120 (60)
Sodium carbonate	washing soda	$Na_2CO_3 \cdot 10H_2O$	286 (143)
Sodium chloride	table salt	$NaCl$	58.5 (58.5)
Sodium hydroxide	lye	$NaOH$	40 (40)
Sodium nitrate	Chile saltpeter	$NaNO_3$	85 (85)
Sodium peroxide		Na_2O_2	78
Sodium silicate	water glass	Na_2SiO_3	122 (61)
Sodium sulfate	Glauber's salt	$Na_2SO_4 \cdot 10H_2O$	322 (161)
Sodium tetraborate	borax	$Na_2B_4O_7 \cdot 10H_2O$	382 (191)
Sodium thiosulfate	hypo	$Na_2S_2O_3 \cdot 5H_2O$	248 (124)
Sucrose	table sugar	$C_{12}H_{22}O_{11}$	342
Sulfuric acid	oil of vitriol	H_2SO_4	98 (49)
Water	water	H_2O	18
Zinc chloride		$ZnCl_2$	136 (68)

*All values have been calculated with atomic weights accurate to the nearest unit. The weight used for chlorine (35.5), however, is accurate to the nearest tenth.

APPENDIX B

The Chemical Elements*

Element	Symbol	Atomic Number	Atomic Weight	Element	Symbol	Atomic Number	Atomic Weight
Actinium	Ac	89	227	Fermium	Fm	100	(253)
Aluminum	Al	13	27	Fluorine	F	9	19
Americium	Am	95	(243)	Francium	Fr	87	(223)
Antimony	Sb	51	122	Gadolinium	Gd	64	157
Argon	Ar	18	40	Gallium	Ga	31	70
Arsenic	As	33	75	Germanium	Ge	32	73
Astatine	At	85	(210)	Gold	Au	79	197
Barium	Ba	56	137	Hafnium	Hf	72	178
Berkelium	Bk	97	(249)	Helium	He	2	4
Beryllium	Be	4	9	Holmium	Ho	67	165
Bismuth	Bi	83	209	Hydrogen	H	1	1
Boron	B	5	11	Indium	In	49	115
Bromine	Br	35	80	Iodine	I	53	127
Cadmium	Cd	48	112	Iridium	Ir	77	192
Calcium	Ca	20	40	Iron	Fe	26	56
Californium	Cf	98	(251)	Krypton	Kr	36	84
Carbon	C	6	12	Lanthanum	La	57	139
Cerium	Ce	58	140	Lead	Pb	82	207
Cesium	Cs	55	133	Lithium	Li	3	7
Chlorine	Cl	17	36	Lutetium	Lu	71	175
Chromium	Cr	24	52	Magnesium	Mg	12	24
Cobalt	Co	27	59	Manganese	Mn	25	55
Copper	Cu	29	64	Mendelevium	M	101	(256)
Curium	Cm	96	(247)	Mercury	Hg	80	201
Dysprosium	Dy	66	163	Molybdenum	Mo	42	96
Einsteinium	E	99	(254)	Neodymium	Nd	60	144
Erbium	Er	68	167	Neon	Ne	10	20
Europium	Eu	63	152	Neptunium	Np	93	(237)

*Source: *Handbook of Chemistry and Physics*, 43rd ed. Copyright 1961 by The Chemical Rubber Publishing Co., Cleveland, Ohio. All atomic weights are represented to the nearest unit. Values in parentheses represent weights of the most stable isotopes.

Appendix B (*continued*)

Element	Symbol	Atomic Number	Atomic Weight	Element	Symbol	Atomic Number	Atomic Weight
Nickel	Ni	28	59	Selenium	Se	34	79
Niobium	Nb	41	93	Silicon	Si	14	28
Nitrogen	N	7	14	Silver	Ag	47	108
Nobelium	No	102	(254)	Sodium	Na	11	23
Osmium	Os	76	190	Strontium	Sr	38	88
Oxygen	O	8	16	Sulfur	S	16	32
Palladium	Pd	46	106	Tantalum	Ta	73	181
Phosphorus	P	15	31	Technetium	Tc	43	(99)
Platinum	Pt	78	195	Tellurium	Te	52	128
Plutonium	Pu	94	(242)	Terbium	Tb	65	159
Polonium	Po	84	210	Thallium	Tl	81	204
Potassium	K	19	39	Thorium	Th	90	232
Praseodymium	Pr	59	141	Thulium	Tm	69	169
Promethium	Pm	61	(147)	Tin	Sn	50	119
Protactinium	Pa	91	231	Titanium	Ti	22	40
Radium	Ra	88	226	Tungsten	W	74	184
Radon	Rn	86	222	Uranium	U	92	238
Rhenium	Re	75	186	Vanadium	V	23	51
Rhodium	Rh	45	103	Xenon	Xe	54	131
Rubidium	Rb	37	85	Ytterbium	Yb	70	173
Ruthenium	Ru	44	101	Yttrium	Y	39	89
Samarium	Sm, Sa	62	150	Zinc	Zn	30	65
Scandium	Sc	21	45	Zirconium	Zr	40	91

APPENDIX C

Units of Measurement

The Metric System

10 millimeters (mm.) = 1 centimeter
100 centimeters (cm.) = 1 meter (m.)
1000 meters = 1 kilometer (km.)
1000 grams (g.) = 1 kilogram
1000 milliliters = 1 liter

Metric-English Equivalents

1 inch = 2.54 centimeters
1 meter = 39.37 inches
1 liter = 1.06 quarts (U.S. liquid)
1 quart = 0.946 liters
1 gram = 0.035 ounce
1 ounce = 28.35 grams

Temperature Conversion

To change degrees Fahrenheit to degrees centigrade, subtract 32 from the degrees Fahrenheit and multiply the difference by 5/9.

To change degrees centigrade to degrees Fahrenheit, multiply the degrees centigrade by 9/5 and add 32 to the product.

To change degrees centigrade to degrees Kelvin, add 273 to the degrees centigrade.

Index to Illustrations

Alcohol burner, 54
Alcohol lamp, wide-flame, 54

Balance: beam, 66; suspended pan, 67
Beam balance, 66
Biological specimens: how to transfer, 100; storage box for, 45
Burettes, 88
Butterfly storage, 74

Chemicals, how to weigh out a required amount, 86
Chromatography, a simple experiment in, 10
Clamp and test tube holder, 63
Cover slips, 51

Displacement pan, 65
Distillation condenser, 85
Draining rack for glassware, 60
Dropper tip, 83
Dry cells, 35
Drying and sterilizing oven, 56

Electric heater, 55
Electricity, a low-voltage, direct-current source of, 35
Experiment, another simple, 12

Filter, how to, 96
Funnel support, 63
Fuse, installation of, 21

Galvanometer, 75
Gases, a displacement pan to collect, 65
Gas generator, 85
Glassware draining rack, 60
Glass tubing: how to bend, 82; how to cut, 80
Graduate made from an olive bottle, 58

Incubator, 71
Insect cage, 72
Insect killing jar, 73
Insect spreading board, 73

Laboratory bench: completed, 27, 30; frame for, 28
Laboratory plan, a sample, 24

Microscope, a water drop: making, 11; using, 12
Moth storage, 74

Oven, drying and sterilizing, 56

Pipettes, 88
Platform, a protective, 19

Ring stand and rings, 62

Screening a lab for privacy, 22
Shelf arrangement: for a biology lab, 31; for a physics or earth science lab, 31
Shelves, an easy way to fasten, 31
Slide, a hanging drop, 102

Table, strengthening a drop-leaf, 26
Test tube generator, 85
Test tube holder, 63
Test tube racks: wire, 59; wooden, 59
Test tubes: how to heat, 99; how to hold in a clamp, 98
Tripod, a tin can, 61

Ventilating a lab: with a window, 20; without a window, 20

Wash bottle, 85
Water supply jug, 34
Weighing a chemical, 86
Weight of a substance, how to find, 87

Index to Materials, Procedures, and Experiments

Acids: containers for storing, 42; neutralizing, 37; preparing solutions of, 90

Acids and bases, how to distinguish, 107

Alcohol lamp: commercial, 52; homemade, 52, 53–55

Ammeter, 52

Analytical balance, 88

Asbestos paper, 20, 32

Atomic weight, 91

Balance and weights, commercial, 51

Balance and weights, homemade: how to make 67–70; how to use, 70–71, 84–88

Beakers, 48

Beetles, mounting of, 101

Bench, laboratory (see laboratory bench)

Biological specimens: containers for, 44–46; collecting and handling, 98–101; disposal of, 38; labeling of, 45–46; microscopic study of, 101–103

Biology laboratory, 18, 24, 29

Boiling point of a solution, 109

Bunsen burner, 51

Burettes, 88–89

Chemical compounds, color of, 109

Chemicals: containers for, 40–44; disposal of solid, 37; disposal of liquid, 37; needed in laboratory, 18, 76; standards of purity, 76; weighing of, 84–88

Chemical substances: identification of, 109; why some burn, 109

Chemistry laboratory, 18, 29

Chromatography, 9–10

Closed environmental system, 112

Clothespin clamp, 33

Clouds, formation of, 116

Containers for biological specimens, 44–46

Containers for chemicals: cleaning of, 42–43; general specifications, 40–41; labeling of, 43–44; sources for obtaining, 40, 41–42

Containers for equipment and supplies, 47

Containers for mineral specimens, 46–47

Corks, 50, 83–84

Craters, formation of, 116

Crucible, 50

Cupboards, 30–32

Displacement pan, 64–67

Doppler effect, 117

Draining rack for glassware, 60–61

Dropper tip, 82

Dry cells, 36

Drying and sterilizing oven, 56–57

Electrical cell, chemical components of, 110

Electrical outlets, 34, 18

Electric heater, 55

Electricity, 34–36

Electric meters, 52

Environment, adjustment of organism to changes in, 110

Equivalent weights, 94–95

Erlenmeyer flask, 48

Evaporating dish, 50

Filtering, 95–97

Filter paper, 95

Fire hazards, 14; precautions, 20

Fire extinguishers, 21

Fireproofing, 20, 32

Flasks, 48–49

Floors, protective platform for, 19

Florence flask, 48, 96
Formula weight, 91–92, 116
Freezing point of a solution, 109
Funnels, 49, 64
Fuses, 21

Galvanometer, 52, 53; homemade, 75–76; string, 53
Gas, relative velocity and pressure of a flowing, 114
Gas burners, 36
Gas generator, 64–66
Gas supply, 36
Glass, disposal of broken, 38
Glass slides and cover slips, 51
Glass tubing, 49; connecting, 83–84; cutting and bending, 79–83; disposal of broken, 83; heating, 81–82; making dropper tip, 82
Glassware, 57, 48–49, 51; connecting, 83–84; heating, 97–98
Glassware draining rack, 60–61
Gyroscope, use of to keep a rocket on course, 117

Heat: effect of surface color on absorption of, 115; relation to temperature, 113
Heaters, 19, 51–52
Hot plate, 52

Ignition boat, 50
Incubator, 71
Inflammable liquids, 14, 37
Insect cage, 72
Insecticides, effect of, 111
Insect killing jar, 72
Insects: mounting of, 101; observation of, 111
Insect spreading board, 74, 101
Iron, what makes it rust, 108

Labels, 43, 44, 45
Laboratory bench, 23–38; building, 25–29; converting a drop-leaf table, 26; dimensions of, 25; sketch before building, 23–25
Life in space, 118
Limewater, 106

Magnetic field, strength of, 113
Mass, measurement of, 115
Materials, 76–78
Meniscus, 89
Metals, how they differ from non-metals, 107
Microscope, commercial, how to test before buying, 50–51
Microscope, water drop, how to make and use, 10–11
Microscope slide, preparing, 101–103
Mineral specimens, 46–47, 115
Molar solutions, 91–93
Molecules, size of, 107–108
Multimeter, 52

Normal solutions, 93–95

One-celled organisms: learning behavior of, 112; sensitivity of to changes in temperature, 110

Paint, chemical resistant, 28
Pendulum, relation between weight of and period of swing, 114
Percentage solutions, 90–91
Pipettes, 88–89
Plants: chemical structure of parts, 112; classification of, 110; effect of chemicals on, 111; water transport in, 111
Plastic jug sink, 33
Platform, 19–20
Polarized light, effect of certain materials on, 114
Poison, 44–45
Porcelainware, 50
Propane burner, 36, 51
Purity, standards of chemical, 76

Radiation, detection of, 118
Ring stand and rings, 61–62
Rocks, 115
Rubber tubing, 49
Rust, 108

Safety, rules of, 13–15
Salt, 76
Satellite, relation between velocity of and radius of orbit, 117

Scrap paper, 36
Screen for privacy, 21
Shelves, 29–32
Sink, plastic jug, 33
Slides, preparing for live specimens, 101–103
Solute, 89
Solutions: calculating and preparing, 89–95; molar, 90–91; normal, 93–95; percentage, 90–91
Solvent, 89
Solvents, biological, 77
Sound waves, reflection of, 114
Spaceship, measuring velocity of, 117
Stains, biological, 77
Stoppers: cork, 50; ground-glass, 42; rubber, 50, 83
Streams of water, formation of crooked, 116
String galvanometer, 53
Sugar, 76
Supports and clamps, 61–62

Table, 25–26; drop-leaf, 26
Telescope, relation between magnifying power and focal length of lenses, 117

Temperature, relation to heat, 113
Test tube holder, wire, 63
Test tube racks: wire, 59; wood, 58
Test tubes: general specifications, 48; heating, 97–98
Thistle tubes, 49
Time, measuring, 103–104
Tripod, 61
Tubing: glass, 49; rubber, 49
Turntable for measuring time, 103–104

Ventilation, 18, 20, 32
Voltmeter, 52
Volumes, measuring, 88–89

Wash bottle, 95
Waste disposal, 36–38
Water: composition of, 108; distilled, 34, 90; soil capacity of, 115; tap, 90, 100; transport in plants, 111
Water supply, 32–34
Weights, balance and, 51
Wing tip for gas burner, 81
Wire gauze screening, 98
Worms, movement of, 111